Mythbusters

Bowvayne

Nut Cases

TRUE STORIES

Elfshot Productions

MYTHBUSTERS – NUT CASES
by Bowvayne

Copyright © Bowvayne 1993

Published by Elfshot Productions
Front cover photograph by Robert Thurston-Hopkins
Typesetting and Graphics: JH Graphics Ltd

Mythbusters and all character names and the distinctive
likenesses thereof are trademarks owned by Bowvayne.

Printed by Cox & Wyman Ltd

ELFSHOT Productions
Books, Scripts, Films, Records, Videos.
PO Box 109
Rustington
LITTLEHAMPTON
West Sussex
England BN16 3BF

ISBN 1 898412 00 6

ABOUT THE AUTHOR

Bowvayne's exact origins are a mystery. Legend has it that he was born somewhere in England twenty odd years ago – but who knows? He spent most of his teens in Australia but later travelled the world, living in West Germany and Singapore. On his return to England in the early 1980s he struck up a friendship with pop star Donovan who encouraged him to transform some of his lively, imaginative song lyrics into a fantasy story. The result was the children's novel, The Forbidden Jewel, 'a whodunnit in Wonderland'. The book was endorsed by popular singer Kate Bush who said; 'If you like adventure, fantasy and magic then this is the book for you . . .' It was on a journey through Wales that he acquired his name. He met an old man sitting on a mountainside who claimed to be a wizard. The man performed astonishing feats such as levitating and calling scores of wild animals to him with the simplest movement of his hands. He dubbed the young man 'Bowvayne', which means 'mystical one' in some Ancient Tongue. What the wizard told him in their twelve hours together will be retold in the soon-to-be-completed adult novel, Ymbryllnior, a magic brew of old lore and parallel faerelven worlds. Surely this chance meeting must have at least partly inspired him to create Mythbusters a few years later, also with its elements of adventure, bizarre encounters and the inexplicable. His second novel was a '20th century fairytale' entitled All Manner Of Magic. An instant hit, it became the bestselling children's book at the 1990 Singapore Book Fair. Also around this time he completed five commissioned stories for an Australian publisher. In late 1987 he and his fellow Mythbusters began their trek of the globe in search of the world's greatest mysteries. They research various myths and personally investigate the validity of the tales. The first Mythbusters book, First Cases, was published in 1991. This is the second book in the series. Currently, several more Mythbusters books are planned, as well as a record and a TV series; they span Europe, Asia, North America, South America, Australasia, Africa, Antarctica, the Arctic circle and the bottom of the deepest oceans. And maybe one day, outer space. . . ?

BOOKS IN THE SERIES

Mythbusters – First Cases
Mythbusters – Nut Cases
Mythbusters – Suit Cases (coming soon)

DEDICATIONS

First, to Tony Adlam for being a first-class editor. Honorary Mythbuster, Annie. Ian Digweed for stalling cars beyond the call of duty. Kate Gorman for becoming the latest to join our exclusive club. Les Hill for using the same word to describe Ian Digweed as I do. Sue McCabe for her tremendous enthusiasm. Also to Chris Strange: Do hurry up and get here, Chris! And finally, the Tooting & Mitcham Balinese Nose-Flute & Basket-Weaving Club.

MYTH: Traditional narrative usually involving supernatural or fancied persons etc. and embodying popular ideas on natural or social phenomena.

The Concise Oxford Dictionary.

'The universe is full of magical things patiently waiting for our wits to grow sharper.'

Eden Phillpotts

Some names and places in this book have been changed to protect anonymity – after all, not everyone wants to be accused of being as crazy as the Mythbusters are!

CONTENTS

The Mythbusters   10

THE GHOST AND THE GRAVEYARD   11
THE ROC   37
CLAPHAM WOOD REVISITED   69

(Over the past six years, there have been two hundred and seven Mythbuster cases. In many of them nothing remotely interesting happened. In these three stories, something did . . .)

Mythbusters – serious fun

THE MYTHBUSTERS

BOWVAYNE

Eternal optimist. Enthusiastic about Mythbusters to the point of lunacy! Daring – but sometimes foolhardy. The writer and leader of Mythbusters is in his mid-twenties. He is slim with long fair slightly curly hair that frames a foxy face. Striking brown eyes. Loves pancakes, chicken drumsticks and practical jokes. Ambitions include wanting to travel in space and finding out where pens go once you've put them down.

IAN DIGWEED

Clumsy. Accident prone. Graceful as a hippopotamus in stilettos walking a tightrope. Expert at impaling himself on fences, silly walks and stalling cars. He joined the Mythbusters as the official driver of its getaway car. Skinny, a little over six feet tall, short, dark brown hair and a mighty beak of a nose. He is 20 years old. Ambition is to visit another planet.

CHRIS STRANGE

Fusspot. Likes to dot every 'i' and cross every 't'. Is in his late twenties. Puppy dog blue eyes. Slightly receding short brown hair. Slim, six feet tall. Renowned glutton. Will eat anything that doesn't move – and sometimes things that do. On his days off he pampers himself with ice creams, jam and scones and likes nothing more than passing the time with his bulldog, Nero. Practical by nature, his pockets are always crammed with everything from sherbet ('to keep the sugar levels up') to complex technological gadgets.

An exciting new development to Mythbusting expeditions is the idea of a celebrity Guestbuster accompanying the Mythbusters on one of their exciting adventures. This book's Guestbuster is:

LES HILL

Intelligent. Headstrong. Has his own theories and ideas about everything. Razor-sharp sense of humour that makes fools look even more foolish. He is 19 years old. A star in the Aussie soap 'Home & Away'. James Dean lookalike with piercing blue eyes. Loves the dark and the mysterious. Ambition is to find out how many mysteries Bowvayne made up as an excuse to go adventuring!

Now you know who the Mythbusters are, come and join them on their 'Nut Cases'.

(prepared by CS)

THE GHOST
AND
THE GRAVEYARD

MYTHBUSTERS WORKSHEET

CASE: The Ghost And The Graveyard

CODE: 0010z 301091

LOCATION: The Melbourne Cemetery, Victoria, Australia

MYTHBUSTERS: Bowvayne
Ian Digweed
Chris Strange

TERRAIN: Roughly a mile square of gently undulating ground, comprising long tussocky grass and weathered gravestones.

TEMPERATURE: 25°C–10°C

DIFFICULTIES: Investigating the stone-cluttered, uneven ground after dark.

SIGHTINGS: Two confirmed sightings of the ghost Red Rogan. One in the 1890s by Marie Le Saux. One in 1991 by Marie's great-granddaughter.

ACTION: Establish whether Red Rogan's ghost really exists. Photograph it with spirit-cameras.

ONE

Young dancer Marie Le Saux bows her head and weeps before the gravestone of her departed husband. Engraved there is:

GOD GIVETH.
GOD TAKETH AWAY.

BORN 1866
DIED 1891

R.I.P.

Why didn't God take someone four times my husband's age away instead, she thinks bitterly. He has been in the ground two months now, killed in a fight over her. At home, her baby,

George, waits. Ah, a lifetime of struggle and sadness lies ahead.

The afternoon sun is hot. A gust of wind from the desert swirls about this sheltered patch of the cemetery, bowing a clump of skinny eucalypts. Abruptly Marie tenses. There is a strange quality to the breeze, a heady enchantment of wildflowers. It makes her think of the French meadows of her childhood. Autumn orchards. The first flowers of spring. The scents befuddle her senses . . .

She hears footsteps. Startled from her reverie, she spins round. A tall, dark-haired man stands before her, eyes like emeralds and something Romany in his appearance. He is the most handsome man she has ever seen. He smiles a smile so dazzling it warms her heart. Then she is afraid. Where has she seen him before?

He smiles again, dispelling her fears.

'Come now, you must mourn no more. You will not bring him back. Jacques is quite content to wait for you on The Other Side. You will dwell here on this earth for such a short time that it may as well be a blissful stay . . .'

'H-How do you know my husband?' Marie asks falteringly.

'We were very much alike, your husband and I. So much in common. So many struggles for the same things . . .' The enchanted breeze of wildflowers and autumnal scents envelopes them both. 'Would you like me to stay with you awhile and talk?' Marie nods dreamily. Mesmerised, she allows him to take her arm.

They walk a short distance and sit beside another new gravestone. The air is oppressive now. But the lovely young dancing girl is captivated by this mysterious man who still hasn't introduced himself. Absently she thinks he's teasing her, making her feel guilty, because she should know him.

They talk about Jacques, baby George, herself and her dancing. But all the while she is luxuriating in the presence of this man. She would serve him the rest of her days and be blissfully happy. There could not be another in the world such as he . . .

The shadows of the tombstones grow long. A chill of evening is in the air.

'Have we spoken for so long?' she says in sudden surprise.

'Yes, we have, my love. And now we must part.' Her face fills with grief and pain at the thought of losing him. 'But not forever, Marie. You must meet me here at this time two weeks today, and seal your promise with a kiss.'

He puts his strong arms around her.

'Yes, I promise I will come,' she says.

Their lips touch. Now she KNOWS who he is. Oh, dear God in Heaven, help me! The man's lips turn hard and bony. The stench of death and decay hangs in the air. She finds herself in the arms of a skeleton.

The truth dawns on her. Yes! She has embraced her husband's killer, himself killed in the brawl over her. She faints.

An unearthly fever grips her, eventually forcing her to keep her promise to the ghost. On the very day at the very time she arranged to meet him she is taken to the Melbourne Cemetery and buried there.

TWO

Like a flying lizard drifting down from the jungle canopy, the Boeing 747 descends into Tullamarine Airport outside Melbourne, Australia. Mythbuster Bowvayne looks eagerly out of one of its small rectangular windows. The sunrise is a spectacular burnished gold. He disembarks and wheels his suitcases through customs.

Outside the terminal, fellow Mythbuster Chris Strange is waiting. 'The plane was seven minutes late,' he says by way of a greeting. He has been in Australia for several weeks, conducting an initial investigation.

'How are you, you old fusspot?' Bowvayne replies affectionately, looking baggy-eyed from the long flight.

'Not bad apart from dehydration of my cerebral fluid causing a subsequent and agonising rubbing of brain on cranium.'

Bowvayne laughs loudly. Strange grips his temples and winces.

Bowvayne affects a stentorian voice. 'You mean you've got a hangover!' Still grinning, he says, 'Beer, whisky, or wine gums?'

'All three,' Strange whispers feebly.

They stagger across the carpark to the latest Mythvehicle, a four-wheel drive Land Rover nicknamed the Mythrover. They toss the seven suitcases into the back.

'Hey! You've forgotten your sticky labels,' Strange says accusingly. 'They're supposed to be on your cases.'

'Wrong colour scheme. They didn't match my luggage,' retorts Bowvayne, quick as a whip.

'Ah, good point,' Strange concedes. He makes a mental note to look out for tatty-brown-coloured sticky labels. Oh, and some faded tartan ones too.

Bowvayne is out of trouble, for now. But he's still got to tell Strange their matching sandwich boxes are at the bottom of Loch Ness.

Strange drives them in the direction of Melbourne, a little over half an hour away. The early October morning is becoming grey and overcast, freckled with rain. Bowvayne babbles excitedly about their latest case, a dragon hunt. Strange nods mechanically, concentrating on the driving and his headache.

Soon Bowvayne is being hustled into Mythbase (Oz)-1, the top secret headquarters and nerve-centre of the Mythbusters entire Australasian operation; it is a white weatherboard house in Brunswick Street, North Fitzroy, a suburb just outside the city.

'Get inside quick. This place is top secret,' Strange hisses urgently, glancing over to the nearby cricket ground. 'And no telephoning the Pizza Palace Home Delivery Service. I don't want anyone to find out *this* address!' Then he grumbles away to himself, tottering inside with all seven cases.

Bowvayne sips a mug of tea and munches on crumpets dripping in melted butter. Contentedly, he sinks deeper into his easy chair.

The room is a mixture of domestic lounge and ancient pagan site. The television and video are crowned with bizarre wooden death masks. An African burial pole seems to sprout from a cheap glass-topped coffee table. Even more incongruously, a set of sacrificial knives from a lost city of the Aztecs is lying next to a poster of Daffy Duck, who is sweating nervously. Only a lunatic could create a room like this.

'Our new office is great, isn't it,' Strange says heartily, popping some Aspros.

'Come on, Chris,' Bowvayne says impatiently, leaning forward in his chair. 'I've just flown twelve thousand miles. Where's this ghost? Spirited away?'

The vein in the middle of Strange's forehead pumps up as he says excitedly, 'What we have right here in Melbourne is the best chance we'll ever get of sighting, photographing and proving to the world that ghosts really exist. It's a remarkably similar tale to something in that old book by Elliott O'Donnell, "Ghosts". This particular family claims to have been targeted by a spirit for over a hundred years. It seems fairly unlikely that they would know O'Donnell's old story . . .'

'But where?'

Strange pauses for effect. 'Wwwell . . .' he teases. Then, when Bowvayne begins to twitch visibly with frustration, 'The ghost is called Red Rogan. And he haunts Melbourne Cemetery!'

A sudden knock on the door makes Bowvayne jump. 'Are you expecting anyone?'

'Yes – it could very well be the latest Mythbuster! He's on holiday out here but he's English.' Strange answers the door. 'Ah,' he says to the stranger. 'Come in.'

There is a hesitant, bumbling fool framed in the doorway. 'I was-er-. . . wasn't quite sure where the Mythbuster office was, so I asked for directions at the Pizza Palace.' He is skinny, a little over six feet

14

tall, with short, dark brown hair and a mighty beak of a nose. Small, round mirror shades rest on the bridge of the beak and a peak-at-the-back baseball cap give him a rather jaunty appearance. He is an applicant for the Mythbuster post of specialist driver. He continues to hover uncertainly.

But the two Mythbusters are affecting their most pompous Mr Employer looks. They have resumed their slouching in easy chairs.

'Name?' asks Bowvayne.

'Ian Digweed.'

'Is that your real name or a pseudonym?'

Digweed is incredulous. 'You've got to be joking. If I was going to choose something other than my real name it would be Falconer or Buckingham – not Digweed!' Bowvayne jots this in his notebook.

It is Strange's turn. 'What makes you think you're qualified for the job? We've already had to sack one Mythbuster for laziness, incompetence and self-importance,' he says self-importantly.

Digweed relaxes. He's got them now, he thinks. But he says, 'I'm a trained racing car driver. I've driven on the Formula One Grand Prix courses at Brands Hatch and Silverstone.'

Four Mythbuster eyebrows arch heavenward. The pair are thinking the same thing: He's only a couple of right answers away from getting the job.

Bowvayne is openly friendly to the 'new boy' now. 'Do sit down, Mr Digweed. Now what interests you about the unknown?'

'I don't know, because it's unknown. Ha ha ha!'

The Mythbusters write 'clever-dick' in their notepads.

'But seriously,' Digweed continues, 'I've always

15

been fascinated by UFOs. And all those stories about there somewhere being extra-terrestrials frozen in ice right here on Earth.'

'Great! That fascinates me too,' Bowvayne enthuses.

Strange gives the interviewee his most penetrating stare. 'Do you ever run away or panic under pressure?'

'Occasionally.'

'Good, because we do,' Strange says drolly.

Bowvayne's turn again. 'What else have you done apart from drive cars?'

'I was a trainee chef . . .' begins Digweed.

'Really?' Strange interrupts, thinking of his all-important stomach. He jumps to his feet excitedly. 'Do you know how to make mixed bean salad or breadfruit curry?' Bowvayne groans in dismay.

'Yes I do,' lies Digweed.

'You're in, Mr Digweed,' says Strange, shaking hands with him vigorously.

THREE

The Melbourne night is cool and still and full of stars. An old green tram clatters to a halt with all the grace of a pneumatic drill, surprising passers-by who are used to trams being on strike. The silver gulls that wheel overhead resemble phantoms as they are captured in the city lights.

Richelle Le Saux clambers unsteadily into the tram, adjusting the school satchel on her shoulders. It is just another night of investigation for this seventeen-year-old student and hitherto unbeliever in ghosts and scoffer at spirits.

Her family have told her of an evil ghost that killed her great-grandmother a hundred years before, and of a gypsy-curse that is upon any member of the Le Sauxs who visits the cemetery. Not that Richelle believes a word of it. But to this intelligent, inquisitive girl whose half-term entertainment normally consists of discos and talking about boys, investigating this ancient family legend draws her as a Venus Fly Trap does a fly.

She scales the tall cemetery fence and lands on the other side with all the sure grace of a cat. Then, taking a hand-drawn map and a torch from her satchel, she creeps forward. This is the eleventh time she has trespassed into the boneyard after dark but she still checks the map, since it becomes a bewildering place late at night. Carefully onward. She's close now.

Suddenly, she has a psychic inkling. Something strange and inexplicable and spooky is about to happen . . .

And then, she sees it! In the midst of a dim light is a free-floating phantom. There is a swirl and a flurry of a crimson cloak. The light brightens to blinding brilliance. In this rectangle of light framed by his gravestone the ghost of Red Rogan comes into sharp focus.

Terrified, Richelle takes a step backwards. Stumbles over a crumbling headstone. Lands heavily on her back. Her breath is knocked from her. 'No no no!' she gasps.

But the ghost's face is almost touching hers. Ready to seal their meeting with a kiss . . .

FOUR

Springtime in Spring Street, Melbourne. There is a spring in the Mythbusters' steps. The city itself is on the Yarra River, and at the head of Port Phillip Bay. It is the capital of Victoria, Australia's southernmost mainland state. Melbourne's skyline is like many other modern cities, crowded with competing monstrosities of concrete and glass. But the place has charm too. Tree-lined boulevards, lush parklands, impressive old churches and banks and the old green trams that clatter by with all the grace of pneumatic drills. The three million inhabitants live in the flat surrounding suburbs. These spread out almost to the distant blue hills of the Dandenongs.

Bowvayne, Digweed and Strange walk past the imposing Parliament House, cross Spring Street and see the famous Princess Theatre for the first time. 'Magnificent,' Bowvayne mutters to himself. It is crowned with three great turrets, golden lions and a golden angelic trumpeter gaze down imperiously from on high and on either side of them are stone carvings that look like genie bottles.

They pass beneath the copper awning and enter the theatre. On their right is an impressive colonnade that leads to the auditorium. But they turn left and head straight for the Federici Bar, named after a famous phantom said to haunt the theatre. Bowvayne smiles wryly when he sees 'Phantom of the Opera' is the current show.

Digweed says with a crooked grin, 'There's a couple more spirits here than in most bars!' They struggle through the crowd to buy drinks.

Bowvayne gives Strange a meaningful stare. It has to be his 'round'. The last time Strange bought someone else a drink Jesus was a batsman for Jerusalem. Strange sees his look, and, sulkily, reaches for his purse. It is tucked in his back pocket but attached by a thick chain to his belt. The purse creaks rustily on being opened, an enormous moth flutters out yelling 'Freedom!', then crumbles to dust in midair.

'Iced water?' he asks innocently. 'Or beer? Yes, I thought so.' He calls the barmaid. 'Two ice . . .'

'. . . cold beers!' Bowvayne cuts in quickly.

'And what about you, sir?' she asks, glowering at Strange.

There is a pregnant pause. The pause gives birth . . . to another pause. The barmaid drums her fingers on the counter. 'Can I get you a drink, sir? I've got other customers waiting.'

Another population explosion of pauses. Finally, Strange says, 'Yeah . . .' His voice cracks. Ah, the pressures of spending money.

Bowvayne and Digweed are cringing in embarrassment. Around them is a team of thirsty Australian Rules footballers. In fact they're hemming them in now. 'Hurry up, idiot!' they shout at Strange.

Strange clears his throat. The barmaid looks at him expectantly. A decision . . . 'I had an amphibian in my epiglottis,' he explains.

'What?' Those swizzle sticks in her hands are looking more and more like murder weapons.

'Er, a frog in my throat.' He laughs weakly. Then, seeing her frown, hurries on. 'I'll have a cream sherry and a bag of cashew nuts but if you don't

19

have any cashews I'll have a brandy alexander and a packet of prawn cocktail crisps.'

The harassed barmaid returns several minutes later to slow handclaps from the footballers. She gives Strange a look of thunder and snaps, 'We don't have any cream sherry or prawn cocktail crisps . . .'

Finally, the trio are sitting at a small table. Bowvayne and Digweed sip their beers. Strange has something that looks more like a tropical island than a drink, complete with plastic palm trees, monkeys, fruit and a blue lagoon. They are waiting for Matthew Mann, an ex-employee at Melbourne Cemetery's records department.

A nondescript Mann comes up to their table and introduces himself. He is a bespectacled scarecrow, perhaps thirty-five, in a crumpled brown suit that hangs from his scrawny frame. 'Mythbusters?'

'Busting to bust!' Digweed says grandiloqently. What does grandiloquently mean, Bowvayne wonders. 'Pleased to meet you, Mr Mann,' Digweed continues.

Mann goes up to the counter, buys himself a coffee and sits at the Mythbusters' table. The atmosphere is a noisy hubbub and everyone needs to talk loudly.

'Give us an exact description of what you saw,' says Strange, taking a mini-recorder from the breast-pocket of his shirt.

'Not so much what I've seen but what I've found out.' He sips his drink and brown threads of coffee skin dangle from his front teeth. 'The fateful day I came to tell you about began with me being late for work. The trams were on strike! I was hurrying across the cemetery to the old house which serves as the office when I caught a momentary flash of a red cloak. Legend tells that Red Rogan always wears such a garment. And the sighting was close to his grave . . .

'This would have been remarkable enough in itself but no sooner had I reached the office than the old cleaner came bursting out of the front door to me, ashen-faced with teeth achatter and buckets aclatter. The poor old girl was in a frightful state. She had been vacuuming in the hallway when her Hoover struck the edge of a loose floorboard. It was, she said, as if she had released "something".

'As soon as she had touched that floorboard, "a handsome gypsy in red" appeared. Quite normal he looked apart from the fact that she could see straight through him. There was a look of interminable misery and sadness on his face. He pointed down at the board, silently beseeching. But poor Mrs Kirkwood saw no more, as she fainted.

'Like a man possessed, I prised the plank further upwards . . . To find a crumbling piece of paper beneath.

'And the note is the most amazing twist of all. For it is the birth certificate of Marie Le Saux's son, George. He was born in 1890 with her maiden name, Pierrot. She must have been unmarried when George came into the world. George's father's name was on the paper to. The name was – Ricard 'Red' Rogan!'

The three Mythbusters gasp in amazement. Everyone talks at once.

'So he wants revenge!' yells Digweed.

'So Marie must have married Le Saux for money and to save her honour!' yells Strange.

'So Rogan's obsessed with the Le Saux descendants as they are all his. The same old story when it comes to ghosts, full of duplicity and betrayal!' yells Bowvayne.

Bowvayne is still puzzled though. 'But what I don't understand is that Red Rogan had his revenge. In the fight between them Le Saux died by Rogan's hand and he claimed Marie with his kiss of death. Strange discovered all this weeks ago. So why does he still haunt the Melbourne Cemetery?'

Mann looks almost ghoulish. 'He has the woman he loved with him. Now he wants the rest of his family!'

Strange shudders. 'Poor Richelle. She's the one in most danger. She should never have gone there.'

'One more question,' mumbles Digweed. 'I was-er-wondering why you asked to meet us here at the Princess Theatre?'

Mann smiles, his mouth all brown and gooey with the coffee skin. 'Good question. I thought it fitting as it's where Marie and Red Rogan met all those years ago. He was a stage-hand when she was a dancing girl.'

'Hmm,' muses Bowvayne. 'So much to consider. Wherever will we start?'

FIVE

Back at Mythbase (Oz)-1, the Mythbusters are chewing their way through one of Strange's famous homemade soups. Bowvayne and Digweed push their bowls away when they can eat no more. 'I feel like a beached walrus,' Bowvayne groans, putting his feet up on the glass-topped table.

Strange is still going strongly, the spoon moving from bowl to mouth in a blur of silver. This gormandizing is punctuated intermittently with ecstatic moaning noises. The telephone hotline interrupts this gluttonous frenzy.

Strange waddles up to the phone, bowl in hand. 'Ah, Richelle. I've been trying to contact you for days. How are you, my dear? I heard you had a terrible fright.' Strange puts his hand over the mouthpiece and whispers to the others. 'It's Richelle. I've been trying to contact her for days. She's fine. She's had a terrible fright.'

'Really?' Bowvayne says drolly.

He goes back to her. '. . . You've been to the cemetery again . . . Swirl of a red cloak again . . . Didn't kiss you, thank goodness! . . . Psychic inkling . . . Bag of cashews . . . Yes, we can . . . Tonight . . . Strange powers . . .' Strange powers another spoonful of soup into his mouth. 'Yes, we can meet you there . . . Fine . . .'

Nine pm. An alarm clock rings. The trio scurry to the Equipment Room. They jump into their black coveralls, strap belts with tape recorders attached – called Sound Belts – round their waists. After climbing into backpacks and fastening down one another's miner's hard hats they check and double check their IRKs. I.R.K. stands for Infra Red Kirlian, an advanced movie camera designed to film, even in total darkness, visitors from the spirit world. They're ready!

The Mythbusters leave the office and clamber into the Mythrover. The aroma of blossom, carbon monoxide and the nearby Pizza Palace Home Delivery Service assault their nostrils. They sneeze simultaneously.

'Damned hay fever,' says Bowvayne.

'Damned car fumes,' says Strange.

'Damned garlic,' says Digweed.

The Mythrover gives a bang-putt-pharrrt and lurches forward. Melbourne Cemetery, here they come!

The cemetery is a huge, sprawling place; easily a mile square of gently undulating ground, long tussocky grass where cicadas chirrup shrilly and tall thin eucalypts sway in the breeze. Like sinister mushrooms, stark and silver in the moonlight, gravestones of granite and marble seem to sprout up ever more quickly the longer the Mythbusters stare, hundreds and hundreds of them, as far as the eye can see. The dead are of many different religions, not just Christian, and the epitaphs in many different languages.

Barring their way in is a ten-foot-high wrought-iron fence, a spear-shaped adornment at the top of each bar. The gates have been locked since six o'clock, when it was still light. As if the wrought-iron fence isn't enough protection, great loops of barbed wire are also tangled along the top. Strange shudders involuntarily.

Bowvayne is studying the awesome fortifications, looking for a weak point. 'Do you think they're trying to keep the dead in or the living out?' Digweed chuckles good-naturedly.

Strange scowls. 'Th-that's not f-funny,' he st-stutters nervously, fumbling with a cigarette and lighter. 'Anyway, I envisaged this problem. That's why there's a ladder in the back of the Mythrover.' The Mythbusters scuttle back to the vehicle. Strange is more jumpy than a frog contemplating a nap in France. His evil soup broth is playing merry hell with his duodenum.

Bowvayne looks at his Mythwatch. 'Richelle is late. We'll give her fifteen minutes.'

Nine-thirty pm. Still no sign of Richelle. Climbing the ladder, they leap into the dark unknown on the other side and land with a sticky splat on solid concrete. After a few groans and rubbing bruised heels and twisted ankles, they get their bearings. Pull the ladder over with them and hide it in some bushes. They pick their way through ancient, crumbling monuments and smashed ruins among overgrown weeds. A bitumen path is just ahead.

'Due north,' whimpers Strange as they trudge onward. Then, more fussily, 'You do realise that if we're caught in here we'll probably be jailed for grave-robbing or something.' He takes a deep drag on his cigarette.

Bowvayne grins. 'Grave-robber. That would look pretty bad on the passports!'

The moon disappears behind dark, scurrying clouds. Now the night is as black as the inside of a coffin.

Bowvayne halts. 'Let's get out our goggles. We never know what we're going to find – and I want to be ready.'

Digweed nods. 'Good idea.'

They take pairs of infra-red goggles from each other's backpacks. As Bowvayne starts groping

25

around in Strange's pack he suddenly looks at him accusingly. 'You've got a flask of your vegetable soup in here! No wonder you were complaining about the backpack being heavy.'

'Emergency rations,' Strange says sheepishly.

They put on their infra-red goggles. Digweed scans over a tree to see honeyeaters sleeping, heads snuggled under wings.

The Mythbusters look vaguely ridiculous, like deep sea fish with flickering filaments for eyes. But they don't care. How exhilarating to see so perfectly in this complete blackness – invaders of the night world with their invisible light! On and on they go, fresh secrets and experiences revealed with every step in this green world.

Strange looks around. 'Not far from Red Rogan's grave now.'

RICARD ROGAN
1860-1891
R.I.P.

The inscription on the tombstone is now pale and weathered. A small monument to a man's life. They stare at it, caught in personal reveries.

Bowvayne shudders. Then breaks the silence. 'I feel as if someone's walking on my grave.'

'Don't say that here,' begs Strange, beads of sweat forming on his forehead.

'But he's right,' Digweed says to Strange. 'I feel as though someone's watching me.'

There's a noise like a cry. The Mythbusters freeze. Something appears from behind the grave. A great shadow rising up from the earth! Looming before them!'

'Hi, it's Richelle Le Saux. You guys are late . . .' she says to the three figures running away so fast you can't see their bottoms for dust.

SIX

Four people walk out of the Mythbusters office to the Mythrover. One is a stunningly attactive girl in her teens. She is slim and petite with honey blonde hair, and her large green eyes have something of the fay about them. With her are three characters who look like they might be pest exterminators or just mad.

They are Richelle Le Saux and the Mythbusters. It is two weeks after their little misunderstanding in the cemetery. Strange is beginning to wonder if all the stories about Red Rogan are just hysterical nonsense. Maybe he is mad to believe a word Richelle says. She is lovely though.

Bowvayne is his normal self; he'll believe anything

once. He is trying to tackle the problem of their shy spook methodically. 'How did you escape Rogan's deadly kiss? Maybe that could give us a clue to finding him.'

Her voice is a breathless whisper. 'Ooh, it was just horrible. After I'd stumbled backwards over that headstone, Red Rogan's swarthy face drifted down almost to mine. I screamed, I think, and turned my torch on to full beam. I don't know what happened to him after I rolled out of the way but he was gone. Lucky.'

Bowvayne nods, satisfied. 'So this ghost reacts to strong light. It's torches off from now on. We don't want to scare it away.'

'Don't we?' Digweed gulps, then lapses back into his nervous silence.

Bowvayne adds smoothly, 'You're pretty brave to still be coming with us after what happened, Richelle.' She smiles wanly.

'Look, I've been thinking,' she begins, swallowing her fear. 'Red Rogan's probably not going to harm me, as according to you guys I'm his great-grand-daughter. I'll go to him as I did before, try and make contact, tell him to Rest In Peace and all that. You can all . . .'

'Far too dangerous. We can't allow it. Don't say another word,' interrupts Strange.

'. . . hide nearby and capture it on film with your IRKs. If anything goes wrong, you'll be ready to dazzle him with your torches.'

'Great plan! Let's go!' Bowvayne says unchivalrously.

'I may as well speak to myself,' Strange speaks to himself.

SEVEN

Midnight. There is a hint of rain in the cool night air. The foursome have just scaled Melbourne Cemetery's fence again. And it's darker than the underside of a bat's wing in there without their torches.

Digweed stands rigid and tense, like an animal sensing danger. 'Right,' Bowvayne says finally. 'Let's split up into pairs. Chris, you and Diggers go straight to the grave. Richelle and I will skirt around the perimeter for a bit and approach Red Rogan's grave from the opposite direction. This will give us a chance to find a hiding place and be ready with the IRKs. If things get out of hand for you we'll turn on torches to scare him off.'

Frowning enviously, Strange watches Bowvayne disappear into the darkness with Richelle.

Bowvayne and Richelle follow the line of the fence. Then head into the middle of the cemetery. Towards Red Rogan's burial place. They hop gingerly over an antique vault and pick their way carefully through an obstacle course of newer marble gravestones.

The wind picks up. The hint of rain becomes a torrent, and hisses harshly as it strikes the smashed ruins and tall weeds. The pair dash beneath a small clump of eucalpyts to escape the downpour.

Richelle squints at her map. 'We're pretty close now.' But they stay under cover five minutes or more.

Bowvayne points up ahead. Through his infra-red goggles he can see a tiny flickering rectangle of light in the distance. Emanating from Red Rogan's grave . . .

Richelle hurries Bowvayne forward. 'Quick! It's just like last time!'

'Let's just hope Diggers and Chris are ready,' Bowvayne says worriedly.

Closer. Closer . . . Oblivious to the fact they're getting soaked. Now they can see his gravestone. Yes, there's that psychic inkling again, Richelle thinks.

There is a crimson tinge to the wind. A moment of intense cold. The rain eases.

Then.

Searing white light explodes from Rogan's headstone. With a twirling flourish of his cloak the gypsy ghost is before them.

He sees Richelle first. When he looks upon Bowvayne, Red Rogan's face twists in jealous rage.

'I think you'd better get out of here,' hisses Richelle.

But Bowvayne is transfixed. He wants to run away but can't, like a rabbit hypnotised by a car's headlights.

EIGHT

'Get out of here!' she begs him now. This ghost is turning decidedly nasty with Bowvayne around.

The Mythbuster gulps. Then addresses him as if Red Rogan is the boxing champion father of his girlfriend. 'We're just good friends – honest!' His eyes grow wide with terror.

Because apparently Rogan doesn't see it that way.

The handsome gypsy face fades – replaced by a hideous skull. Foul and wormy it is, the remaining flaps of skin putrescent and cankered.

Without warning, a bony arm reaches out for the Mythbuster, skeletal fingers click-clacking as they close on nothing. In that split-second Bowvayne hurls himself sideways and backwards, out of reach of the claw of death. 'Turn on the torches! Chris! Diggers! For God's sake!'

No answer.

With a fingernail-curling shriek, the skeleton floats towards him. Desperation grips Bowvayne. He fumbles with his torch. Drops it. It rolls away into the darkness. His last hope gone. Red Rogan's bones loom ever closer, closer to Bowvayne's face. Oh no, not the kiss!

Richelle shouts with great authority, 'Ricard Rogan! Be at peace. We understand why you haunt this place. And I know I am your great-grand-daughter . . .'

At that moment Red Rogan becomes whole again. His handsome gypsy face reappears – and he turns to Richelle and smiles.

Then there is a blinding wall of light. Confusion. Bowvayne runs one way and Richelle another. Digweed and Strange come out of the darkness holding torches.

'Is everything alright?'

'What happened?'

'The ghost! The ghost! Red Rogan is here! Did you film it on the IRKs?' Bowvayne implores, not unhysterically.

Digweed is dreadfully disappointed. 'We took shelter from the rain. We didn't see a thing.'

31

'We didn't think you'd even be here yet!' Strange curses, wild with frustration.

'Let's scout around now; we might still find him,' Digweed says resolutely. The others agree.

'Did anything much happen?' Strange asks Bowvayne and Richelle.

Bowvayne replies with heavy irony. 'You might say that.'

But they search in vain. Red Rogan is gone.

MYTHBUSTER SUMMARY SHEET

I expect everyone reading this knows someone who claims to have seen a ghost. Surely with so many sightings there should be little doubt that they actually exist. But there is doubt. Why?

The answer to this lies in the very nature of the spirit world. They are 'borderline' entities: Existing on the line between reality and fantasy. Sanity and madness. Life and death. Who can speak with conviction of things that dwell in these realms?

But why should ghosts trespass back to this world where they no longer belong? For many reasons. A lover has betrayed them. A false friend has murdered them. They were cheated out of completing a work of great importance by Death. People who lead normal lives seldom return as ghosts (unless danger threatens a loved one still living.) But it is those who feel cheated or betrayed that are the largest percentage of those who 'come back'.

And Red Rogan? He felt cheated of course. He was cheated of the woman he loved, a happy family, and ultimately his life by circumstance. He had no money. Money WOULD have brought him happiness. Jacques Le Saux had money. So he won Marie, little George, everything. Rogan's frustration lived on even after he and Le Saux had fought to the death. But now, a hundred years later, Richelle Le Saux has let him know they recognise him as blood-kin. Red Rogan will Rest In Peace.

We hope.

THE ROC

MYTHBUSTER WORKSHEET

CASE: The Roc

CODE: 001Mal/Sey 220292

LOCATION: The Maldives are over 2000 tiny coral islands scattered across the crystal waters of the Indian Ocean. The Seychelles are 86 incredibly beautiful islands further south, generally larger and more mountainous with tangled forests.

MYTHBUSTERS: Bowvayne
Chris Strange

TERRAIN: Sandy islands with swaying coconut palms. Sparkling lagoons. Coral reefs. Some forest.

TEMPERATURE: 24°C – 33°C

DIFFICULTIES: Occasional high humidity. Occasional sharks, barracudas, moray eels. Constant threat of succumbing to the island paradise, lying in the sun with a cocktail and never wanting to get up again.

SIGHTINGS: Seven over a five year period.

ACTION: Full-scale investigation. Attempt to photograph this truly monstrous bird from Arabian mythology.

ONE

Four hundred miles south west of Sri Lanka lie the
Maldives, over two thousand coral islands scattered
across the crystal waters of the Indian Ocean. It is
true paradise. Bliss. Nirvana. Earthly Heaven.
Heavenly Earth. That is if you like sunburn, salty
water stinging your eyes and sand in your mixed
bean salad.

'This is paradise,' says Bowvayne.

'Yeah, but mate,' Chris Strange whinges. 'There's
sand in my mixed bean salad.'

Both are sitting on the beach in swimming
trunks. Bowvayne gazes across the gleaming white
expanse . . .

'You really need a suntan, Chris.'

. . . then over the gleaming white beach to where
the coconut palms gently nod over a translucent blue
lagoon. The island is so tiny it takes only five
minutes to walk right round it.

Strange applies white zinc creme to his reddening
nose. 'Fancy doing some more snorkelling later on?'

Bowvayne remembers the amazing kaleidoscopic
beauty of the coral reef they had seen that morning.
'Yeah! Great! I'm hoping we might even catch a

glimpse of the famous whale shark. Someone told me they're nearly fifty feet long!'

Strange looks sweaty and nervous. 'A few sea squirts and a shoal of those pink things with polka dots will suit me fine.'

Scurrying down the beach from the hotel is Tim, the Sri Lankan receptionist (and part-time pedlar of cowrie shells for exorbitant prices).

'Hide your money,' Bowvayne sighs. 'He's not still trying to sell you that cowrie shell convertible nail-file and egg-timer, is he?'

'No no. I bought a cowrie shell tobacco pouch from him yesterday.'

The dark, skinny boy struggles down the sand to them, a half-eaten, suspicious-smelling poppadam waving around in one paw, a portable phone in the other.

'Looks as if your take-away's arrived, Bowvayne.'

He is puffing and panting when he reaches the Mythbusters, probably from the weight of dozens of cowrie shell necklaces around his neck, all with price tags on them. 'Telephone, sahs! Telephone!' he jabbers excitedly.

'Thank you, Tim,' says Strange, taking the phone and tipping him. 'Hello? . . .Ah, thanks for calling, Dav . . . Where are you? . . . Malé . . . How many people saw this bird? . . . Definitely remember the location . . . Breadfruit curry . . . We'll be there . . .' He hands the phone back to the Sri Lankan.

Bowvayne's face is an enormous grin. 'They've seen it again, haven't they?'

'Yeah, they've seen it again,' replies Strange. He clambers to his feet and rolls up his Daffy Duck beach towel. 'Come on. Let's go. Dav is in Malé right now.' He struggles to keep his voice even, his innards churning with suppressed tension and anticipation. 'If Dav isn't exaggerating, they've all seen easily the biggest bird in the world!'

TWO

The Mythbusters dash down the beach and push their narrow fisherman's boat over the starched white sand and into the sea. It is made of coconut palm and about fifteen feet long; and its outboard motor coughs asthmatically as Strange pulls the cord, then heads out into the ocean.

The brilliant yellow sun straddles the equator here and it beats down relentlessly. It is hotter than a game of strip poker in the Hellfire Club. Sweat springs from every pore.

'Better put shirts on or we'll get a bad burn,' says Strange. They both pull on white Mythbuster tee-shirts (available from good clothes stores everywhere).

Bowvayne checks his map and compass. 'I reckon it's about a three-hour chug to Malé.'

That journey from their resort to the Maldivian capital is a magical one. A school of dolphins escorts them out of the lagoon. They chatter amiably to the Mythbusters while riding in the boat's bow wave. One leaps out of the water as it swims, another performs a playful somersault. Bowvayne has an overwhelming desire to become one of them.

On the seaward side of the lagoon, hawksbill turtles glide gracefully beneath the wooden boat. All around them the great Indian Ocean breaks upon the sandy shores of the tiny tropical islands, the white horses running up to the coconut palms and bougainvillaea bushes where red and green parakeets squawk and squabble.

Late afternoon. Bowvayne and Strange tie the boat up at the pier in Malé. Although this is the capital, it is little more than a square mile in area. The tiny town is made up of coral-stone houses, and looming in the distance is the huge, three-storey 'skyscraper' with its one hundred and thirty-three minarets.

The pair walk through the sandy streets to the Mijheedhee Magu, the area where the cafes are to be found. The whole place reeks of fish and coconut oil. A wrinkled gnome of a man ambles past them with an enormous, smiling fish hanging over his shoulders. An old crone in a cotton dress is slouched in a shady alley-way, smoking a hookah pipe. Curiouser and curiouser.

They finally find the shopfront sign they are looking for. It is a seedy-looking eating-house with tables and chairs outside. A bedraggled grey parrot in a rusted cage greets them, swearing at Strange in Divehi, the local language.

'I think he likes you,' Bowvayne says, smiling at his partner.

Strange is impatient. 'Do you realise how many thousand miles we've come for this? The amount of red ink I'll have to use on the end-of-month Mythbuster Accounts if this is a wasted trip!'

'Oh, don't worry about all that,' Bowvayne replies airily. He lives his life like a monkey who thinks the world is an enormous banana tree — and never sees the skins.

Strange reflects on the telephone call that brought them here. Soon after the case of The Ghost And The Graveyard, their old school friend, Dav Jayasundera, had phoned Mythbase (Oz)-1 from Malé with a quite incredible tale. While out on a fishing-boat he and a group of friends had been attacked by an enormous bird of prey. Its size and description, added to the fact that the incident occurred in the Indian Ocean, all hinted at something fantastic: that this was the roc of Arabian mythology. This was a case too good to miss, he sugggested, and the Mythbusters should come and meet him in Malé as soon as they could.

Ian Digweed had remained in Australia to continue research on the UFOs of the Nullarbor Plain.

Bowvayne's stomach-radar is searching without success for a plate of chicken drumsticks. A couple of roc drumsticks would suit me fine, he thinks whimsically. 'Let's sit down, Chris. I'm starving.'

'I'm going to have the breadfruit curry,' Strange says decisively.

'You're sure it won't put you over your dinner budget?' Heavy irony.

'Not if I barter skilfully.' Oblivious to heavy irony.

They sit at a table. Bowvayne reads the menu, written exclusively in Divehi script. When a scruffy old waiter with stained teeth shuffles up to them, pen and notepad in his hand ready to take their order, Bowvayne points indiscriminately at something about halfway down the list.

'Breadfruit curry,' Strange says hopefully when it is his turn.

The waiter looks apologetic, signalling that he doesn't understand.

Strange tries again, lapsing into the ridiculous pidgin-style jargon so many tourists try on the natives. 'Er, bleadfluit cully?' The waiter stares back helplessly.

Then to Bowvayne's acute embarrassment, Strange starts playing charades with the hapless Maldivian. First he mimes 'bread'.

Suddenly the waiter is beaming.

Then the Mythbuster pretends to be a piece of fruit falling from a tree by falling from his chair.

The beam becomes a toothy grin. 'Beer?'

'No no no,' says an exasperated Strange. He signals there is something hot in his mouth. Curry. 'Bread. Fruit. Curry. Okay, mate?'

The old fellow laughs uproariously, then indicates he has understood and walks back to the shop.

They hear a familiar booming laugh and look around. It is their Sri Lankan friend, Dav Jayasundera. He strides up to their table, right hand outstretched and booming laugh replaced by a booming voice. 'It's great to see you both.'

Handshakes and greetings over, Jayasundera takes a seat then summons the waiter, making an order in fluent Divehi. The Mythbusters listen jealously.

'Could you get us something to drink, Dav?' Bowvayne asks.

'Sure.' Then to the waiter, 'Kiru sarbat.'

He is a tall, powerfully built man in his mid twenties — a far cry from his childhood when he had the physique of a stick insect on hunger strike — with skin the colour of hazel nuts. His eyes are very dark, calculating, yet there is a hint of warmth in them too. His hair, like the smooth sheen of a raven's wing, frames a handsome, if decadent, face. He wears one of his infamous batik shirts, a bilious clash of purple and yellow.

Even before they have finished with 'small talk', the Maldivian is standing beside them with a heavily-laden tray.

Strange looks expectant. 'I'm really looking forward to my breadfruit curry.'

A glass of kiru sarbat is placed in front of each of them. Bowvayne takes a sip. It has a sweet, milky flavour.

Then the three plates of food are presented. Jayasundera sucks air between his teeth and slouches back in his chair. 'Ah, their bambukeylu hiti is wonderful,' he declares, looking down at his plate.

'But you've got the breadfruit curry!' Strange says accusingly, glowering at his own plateful of fish and herbs.

'Yes I know,' replies Jayasundera. 'That's what bambukeylu hiti means: "breadfruit curry".'

The waiter is grinning pathetically at Strange, like a dog waiting for a pat on the head. The Mythbuster forces a smile through clenched teeth. The Maldivian trots away happily.

Strange looks at Bowvayne's plate. He has the same dish, fish with herbs. 'Do you want to swap, Dav?'

The seasoned vindaloo curry eater thinks for a moment, then, 'No thanks. Too hot for me.'

Bowvayne and Strange both take a mouthful of fish, probably sailfish.

Strange is grumpy. 'What do you mean, "too hot"?

43

It's lukewarm. And if you mean the other kind of hot, it's quite bland.'

'Yes,' agrees Bowvayne. 'Quite bla . . . bla . . . bla . . . bla . . . dy hell!' he finishes, fanning his mouth with his hands.

'Man the pumps! Send for the fire brigade! My mouth's on fire!' Strange gasps. The pair drain their drinks, eyes, mouths, noses and ears streaming from the vicious spice.

'That is called githeyo mirus,' Jayasundera manages to say between booms of laughter. 'Some say it's too hot for the Devil himself!'

Bowvayne wheezes in reply.

Strange fizzles like a dying firecracker.

Later on, after the Mythbusters' dinner-time performance, Strange has regained his dignity. 'Give us an exact description of what you saw,' he says, taking a mini-recorder from the breast pocket of his shirt.

This is what Jayasundera tells them:

THREE

The reflected sunlight glitters diamonds and sapphires in the translucent blue waters of the Indian Ocean. A long wooden fishing-boat skims over the water, the sail flapping wildly about its tall mast.

The group of five Sri Lankans aboard comprises Dav Jayasundera, his girlfriend, his brother, the brother's girlfriend and a female servant. All afternoon they have been fishing for shark and chasing shoals of skipjack tuna – without much success. They are somewhere in the Maldives, the waters of which are more than ninety nine percent of the whole country's area.

Sharp dorsal fins are seen cutting through the sea towards them; the scene of a hundred nightmares. Jayasundera's brother, Gordon, throws a bag of bloodied dead rats into the water. A local fisherman had told them that with this bait you would catch whitetip reef sharks every time.

As the Jayasundera brothers ready fishing-rods, they all see the serried rows of dagger-sharp teeth rip and tear at the bait and each other.

Something momentarily blots out the sun. Dav glances up from the savage scene before him, expecting to see an aeroplane or a flock of birds moving across the sky. He swears aloud and yells to his companions, 'Look! Look! Just look up there!' Four heads look up sharply to where he is pointing. A bird of awesome size circles the boat.

'It is roc,' says the frightened servant-girl.

It senses there is prey in the sea and wheels about for a moment longer. Then swoops downward, an immense black blur with talons.

Is it one of them or a shark that will be its food? With screams of terror they all fling themselves on to the deck. Dav feels a rush of air just above him as the great bird passes overhead. There is a horrifying screech.

The roc rises from the water with a shark in its talons. It flies off in the direction it has come, finally fading from vision.

FOUR

After recounting the incident of a week before, Jayasundera looks at the Mythbusters and shakes his head. 'As you know, I'm not interested in myths and mysteries like you are . . . but this . . . this was something else.' He picks up his glass and swallows the kiru sarbat in one gulp.

'Could you show us exactly where it happened?' Bowvayne asks, eyes shining with the fanatical gleam that normally means trouble for everyone.

'Sure.'

'Right now?'

The big Sri Lankan is doubtful. 'It'll be dark before we get there . . .' he begins.

'Yeah, mate. He's right . . .' Strange begins.

But Bowvayne's mind is made up. 'We don't need to worry about little things like that! Let's go!'

Early evening back at the boat. The trio strap themselves into life-jackets and are soon chugging steadily away from Malé.

Bowvayne has that face-consuming grin on again and is gabbling breathlessly. 'Ihopeyou'rereadyfor thisI'vegotafeelingthisisgoingtobethebigonethebig-gestbirdintheworldwow!'

Jayasundera wonders how he was talked into this.

But Strange is irascible. 'Even if the roc loops the loop for us it's going to be too dark to see anything, let alone take photographs.' As if to prove his point, the sun sinks visibly on the horizon ahead. The sky has become subtle hues of gold, a breathtakingly beautiful scene, filled with the silhouettes of seabirds on the wing.

The boat circles the area where the Sri Lankan

thinks he saw the roc. It has taken them almost five hours to reach this spot. They are in complete darkness although it is still pleasantly warm. Only their torches' powerful beams offer any hint of what is 'out there'.

'I'll drop anchor so we can listen out for a while,' says Jayasundera.

Another hour passes. All they hear is the steady slap-slap of water that rocks the boat from side to side. Jayasundera feels the first nauseous bubblings of sea-sickness from within.

Unaware of their friend's suffering, the Mythbusters are finishing a discussion/wrangle. Bowvayne is thoughtful. 'Where would a roc go at night? The nearest island, perhaps?'

Strange nods. 'That'd be a pretty good guess. It's more likely to be somewhere like that than out here.'

Bowvayne's mind has another straw of hope to clutch at. 'Are there any islands nearby, Dav?'

'There's one less than ten minutes away as it happens,' Jayasundera replies with a casual air that conceals a wave of relief surging over him. He would have done and said anything to get his feet on dry land again, even if it had been infested with tigers. 'I'll take you there now.'

Twenty-five yards from the island, Jayasundera leaps from the boat and swims ashore. He races up the sand and disappears into the darkness.

Bowvayne and Strange look at one another in bafflement.

'He's really going overboard with enthusiasm, isn't he?' quips Strange.

'Yeah. There could have been sharks or anything

in there. I thought I was the only one who did crazy things like that!'

The Mythbusters guide the boat up on to the beach and then drag it further up the sand. They scramble up the talcum power-like sand and move cautiously into the Stygian gloom of the closely-packed coconut palms, all the while hissing, 'Dav! Dav! Where are you!'

Finally, he reappears. Sorry about that, guys. I felt a bit ill,' he mumbles, embarrassed.

'You going to be okay?' Strange asks, concerned.

'Sure,' says Jayasundera. He trips over a fallen tree and lands heavily. 'Sure.'

The trio advance, torches scanning for danger. A flock of startled birds explodes from the trees in a cacophony of beating wings. They all jump.

'If we're frightened by crows, God knows what we're going to do when we find the roc,' Jayasundera says without humour.

There is a heavy thump behind them. They all grip one another tightly. 'The roc?' Strange's voice is hoarse, panicky.

'No. A falling coconut.' They move on.

'Have you ever had the feeling that you're being watched?' trembles Bowvayne, swinging his torch upwards.

'Yeah. Right now,' whispers Strange. His torch beam catches a massive black silhouette. The mysterious creature crashes to the ground some distance away.

'That's it. I'm getting out of here, with or without you,' Strange says in a low voice. This decision is final. He will not be swayed under any circumstances.

'I'm with you, Chris,' hisses Jayasundera.

Too late.

The dark shape leaps at them with a screech that shrivels the hair from their buttocks. In the split-second it is illuminated by their torches, the three of them see a hairy ape dressed in rags. Dark blazing eyes. A sharp and deadly weapon glittering . . .

Someone yells the Mythbusters motto, 'Run away!' They retreat with all the dignity of headless chickens, stopping only to push the boat out to sea.

FIVE

The trio are slumped exhaustedly in the boat as it heads back to the sanctuary of their hotel beds.

Bowvayne is disgusted. 'Who said "run away"? That might've been the photograph of a lifetime.'

'The end of your lifetime, you mean,' says Jayasundera seriously.

'I noticed you'd overtaken me by the time we got to the boat,' Strange points out to Bowvayne.

Bowvayne is unrepentant. 'I just got caught up in the hysteria of the moment. Anyway, what do you think it was back there?'

'I know what it wasn't,' Jayasundera drawls wearily. 'A roc.'

'Maybe it was Robinson Crusoe,' teases Strange. He is almost his old self again (minus the buttock hair).

Bowvayne takes seriously the suggestion that it could have been someone marooned. 'If the name of that place is Treasure Island then we just met Ben Gunn!'

'I've just realised something,' Jayasundera booms, fear coming into his eyes. 'Convicted criminals in the Maldives are set down on uninhabited islands for the length of their sentence. We've probably just run slap-bang into a dangerous prisoner!'

Strange isn't convinced. 'Surely they'd have better security around the place than that?'

'It sounds too cushy to me.' Bowvayne is also doubtful. He adds with a grin, 'Hey, it'd be pretty ironic if you're right though. Tourists paying thousands of pounds to get the same treatment as Maldivian convicts!' Bowvayne and Strange laugh. Jayasundera booms.

'All the same,' the Sri Lankan says finally, 'I say we steer clear of that island from now on. That was one hell of a dagger he had on him.'

After returning Jayasundera to Malé the Mythbusters arrive back at the resort hotel, collapsing into their beds just before eight in the morning.

Noon. A rumpled Bowvayne pads softly from the hotel room, careful not to wake Strange who is snoring like an old kettle. He walks tiredly across the sandy courtyard to the optimistically named Business Centre, basically a broom cupboard housing a fax-machine and a telephone.

Ian Digweed has found some additional information on the legend of the roc and faxed it through to them from Australia. Bowvayne and Strange had left for the Maldives in such a hurry that their normally extensive library research had had to be skipped.

Strange hadn't been pleased with the situation. 'I

think it's sloppy to start a new case without thorough research.' Bowvayne pretended he hadn't been pleased with the situation.

Bowvayne sits on the only chair in the place, a rickety affair, and settles down to read the faxed information. He is enthralled. His imagination runs riot.

The world of Arabian mythology is fabulous and fanciful: cruel kings and pervasive genies, magnificent medieval palaces in harsh, waterless deserts, camels and oases, swarthy, sinister men with hooked noses and scarred faces carrying curved swords, impossibly beautiful women belly-dancing, 'Open Sesame' caves, magical flying carpets and treasure chests spilling over with priceless jewels. Aladdin and his enchanted lamp feature in these stories. As does Ali Baba and the Forty Thieves. And Sinbad the Sailor.

Also featuring mighty among this rich vein of legend are the 'Great Birds' – the griffins of the Caucasus, the phoenix of Arabia, the simurgs of Persia and the giant rocs of the Indian Ocean.

According to the famous Venetian adventurer Marco Polo (1254-1324), the roc inhabits Madagascar and other islands off the east coast of Africa. It is shaped like an eagle but is so huge that each feather is as large as a palm frond. So powerful is the roc that it can carry an elephant in its talons. Contained in the famous collection of Arabic tales, "The Thousand And One Nights", are the seven voyages of Sinbad. The stories are filled with his scrapes with rocs.

Bowvayne exhales heavily. 'Wow! Incredible stuff! Well done, Diggers.'

He races up the steps to the hotel room, flings the door open, yelling, 'Chris! We're going to Madagascar!'

Strange groans, pulls the bedspread over his head and continues snoring. In his sleep he mumbles, 'More red ink. More red ink . . .'

SIX

The Mythbusters walk from their hotel room down to the beach, a Maldivian beach not a Madagascan one. It is three weeks after their midnight jaunt.

They scan the horizon. No sign of Dav. Just a sixty-foot luxury yacht and a kid on a windsurfer.

Strange doesn't like surprises. 'I wonder what Dav meant when he said he'd borrow an old piece of junk from a friend of his uncle's? I'm not sailing in something unsafe.'

Bowvayne has finally got his own way. An investigation spanning the whole Indian Ocean. 'Don't worry, Chris,' he says soothingly. 'When he said "junk" he probably meant as in the Chinese, flat-bottomed variety.'

They put their belongings near the water's edge and sit on suitcases.

Strange is still stubborn. 'It's going to be some floating Rent-A-Wreck; I can feel it in my water . . .'

'Hey! You guys!' booms Jayasundera from the sixty-foot luxury yacht. 'Are you coming aboard or what?'

Strange warms instantly. 'Remind me to get my water changed when we get home,' he says to Bowvayne.

The pair wade out to the yacht with suitcases, fishing rods, scuba gear, binoculars, cameras, compasses, maps, a bag of bloodied dead rats and three rounds of sailfish sandwiches. Jayasundera hauls the Mythbusters and their gear over the silver guard-rail and on to the polished wooden deck.

The interior of the yacht is awesome in its opulence, an air-conditioned cabin and bathroom each, in the finest dark mahogany wood. Also aboard are Jayasundera's Uncle Lalith, an expert sailor, and Adolf the German chef. Even as Bowvayne and Strange bumble round the boat open-mouthed with amazement, Adolf is in the customised kitchen preparing lobster salads.

After unpacking their suitcases and changing into dry shorts, the pair meet back at the yacht's bar. Bowvayne acts as barman and makes them a large gin and tonic with ice and lemon each.

'Shall we make everyone walk the plank and steal the boat?' Bowvayne says, only half joking.

'Alright. Oh, except Adolf,' Strange replies, remembering his all-important stomach. Then, changing subject, 'By the way, Diggers faxed some more stuff through this morning. About the biggest birds, Living and Extinct. He got it out of "The Guinness Book of Records". Here, have a look.'

This is what Bowvayne reads:

BIRD OF PREY. The heaviest bird of prey is the

53

Andean condor (Vultur gryphus) with adult males averaging 20-25lb.

LARGEST WINGSPAN. The wandering albatross (Diomedea exulans) of the southern oceans has the largest wingspan of any living bird, adult males averaging 10ft 4in with wings at full stretch. The largest recorded specimen was a very old male with a wingspan of 11ft 11in, caught by members of the Antarctic research ship USNS Eltanin in the Tasman Sea on 18th Sept 1965. Unconfirmed measurements up to 13ft 3in have been claimed for this species.

FLYING BIRD. The largest known flying bird was the giant teratorn (Argentavis magnificens), which lived in Argentina about 6 million years ago. Fossil remains discovered at a site 100 miles west of Buenos Aires in 1979 indicate that this gigantic vulture had a wingspan of 23-25ft.

'Goodness me, this confirms it!' Bowvayne exclaims, looking up from the faxed pages. 'Dav's bird was bigger than any of these! And it's out here somewhere!' He takes a huge swig on his gin and tonic.

Jayasundera comes down the steps leading below deck and joins them. 'I've got those maps you asked for,' he booms, handing them over. Bowvayne spreads the largest one out across the bartop. Jayasundera pulls up a stool and joins them.

The excited Mythbuster runs a trembling finger down the map. 'So this is it. Next stop the

Seychelles. Then the Comores. Circumnavigate Madagascar. A quick stop in Mauritius. Then return the boat to Colombo, Sri Lanka. We're sure to find the roc and half a dozen other things in that time and . . .'

Strange interrupts, attempting to bring his madcap friend back to the real world. 'It could take months!'

There's that fanatical gleam in Bowvayne's eyes again. 'Yeah, it's great, isn't it?'

But Strange attempts to reason with Jayasundera. 'Surely we've only got this boat for a few days at most?'

'Oh, no,' Jayasundera says blithely. 'We've got it for as long as we want. Uncle Lalith's friend has got a couple more yachts like this!'

Strange looks astounded. He feels surrounded by lunatics. Wonderful, irresponsible lunatics. If you can't beat them join them, he thinks. He says, 'Yipppppeeeeeeeeeee!'

After a magnificent lobster each for lunch sat up on deck, Bowvayne asks the Sri Lankans, 'When are we leaving?'

'It is not so simple,' the portly Lalith replies, sipping a glass of chilled white wine. He is in his late fifties, small and grey-haired, but there is an immense dignity in his demeanour. 'A hundred subtleties of wind direction and water current have to be considered . . .'

The hotel receptionist, Tim, makes a bee-line towards them down the beach, brandishing his range of expensive and completely useless cowrie shell souvenirs.

'. . . And we're leaving right this second,' says the old sailor. He lurches to his feet and winds in the anchor frantically.

Before long the yacht is cruising steadily south, past hundreds of coral reefs and tiny uninhabited islands. Further down the Indian Ocean than the Mythbusters have ever been before.

SEVEN

Somewhere along the chain of low coral atolls, between the Maldives and the Seychelles, the luxury yacht has dropped anchor. It is six days later. Dav, Lalith and Adolf are fishing for their lunch. Bowvayne and Strange are about to go snorkelling.

The Mythbusters are going to jump overboard when Strange remembers something. 'Adolf, do you know how to make breadfruit curry?'

'Vot iss das?' the chef asks apologetically.

Strange starts playing charades with the hapless German. First he mimes 'bread'.

'And this is a piece of fruit falling into water,' Bowvayne says, giving his friend a tremendous push overboard.

The pair swim around the reef, among the astonishing variety and number of colourful underwater creatures. The yellow and blue clown fish reclining in the toxic tentacles of sea anemones. Wrass, goby, damselfish, butterflyfish, triggerfish, surgeonfish, lionfish, goatfish, cowfish, unicornfish.

Vast shoals passing like a dazzling dream before their eyes.

Parrotfish loudly crunching the hard coral in their powerful jaws. A majestic manta ray gliding overhead like an extra-terrestrial on some timeless journey between the stars. A moray eel lurking in a crack in the coral. Warily, the two humans pass them by.

There is a sudden flurry of activity all along the reef. Fish darting in all directions. Large, dark phantom-silhouettes loom just above the Mythbusters. A dead rat plummets between them, down to the ocean floor.

Bowvayne is appalled. Someone incredibly stupid has become impatient at 'hooking' nothing for lunch and thrown in the shark bait. He sees Strange silently mouthing the word 'Dav' and rolling his eyes in disgust. The pair realise those phantom-silhouettes are sharks. Hammerhead sharks.

Bowvayne's mind, nearly unhinged with fear, treats him to the spectacle of being torn apart in an orgy of gore and maiming by those sharks. He follows Strange as he dives deeper, thinking he has a plan.

Strange doesn't have a plan. In blind panic he's hurled himself as far from the sharks as possible.

Now the Mythbusters are floating helplessly upward. The hammerheads move closer. Until now I didn't realise it was possible to break out into a sweat while underwater, Bowvayne thinks, a hint quixotically.

Their heads appear from out of the ocean. Both gasp for breath, looking around frantically for the sharks.

'W-where. . . ?' stutters Strange.

Bowvayne is puzzled. 'Gone. Some-something frightened them off.'

Thankful for their good luck, they swim back to the boat, three hundred yards away. Then they see it. A momentary glimpse of a mighty bird retreating from vision, a hammerhead shark in its talons. Heading for the island on the horizon.

EIGHT

'Quick! Quick!' Strange yells to the crew as he scrambles back on deck.

Bowvayne is right behind them. 'Follow that bird!'

There is a lot of excitement on board. Lalith steers the sleek white vessel straight for the island ahead. Everyone takes it in turns to look through the only pair of binoculars handy — even though there's no sign of the bird now.

'I think I saw it,' Jayasundera says hopefully.

'But it could've been anything,' says his uncle.

'Definitely the roc, definitely,' Bowvayne says definitely.

Strange agrees with him. 'Seagulls don't carry off hammerhead sharks!'

All five of them think they're sounding calm and rational but are in fact babbling like children who have caught a glimpse of Santa Claus. Even dour old Adolf is chattering away happily to himself in German.

'Faster!' Bowvayne urges the skipper, dancing around the deck like a marionette.

Strange leaps down the steps below deck in a single bound to sling the necessary equipment for the investigation into his backpack.

The yacht is close to the shoreline now. The Mythbusters and Jayasundera leap overboard. The temperature must be well into the nineties, even though evening isn't far away, and the shock of the water right up to their armpits is a pleasant one. They wade through the surf, Strange holding the backpack above his head.

A thousand miles off the east coast of Africa, this beautiful island is perhaps five miles long. Beyond the palm-fringed beach it rises abruptly, the interior becoming mountainous and lush with vegetation.

The trio march up the sandy white beach to the lofty palms. Clamber up an outcrop of massive rectangular and square-shaped boulders, the largest more than twenty feet tall. It is a difficult fifteen minute climb. Knees are grazed and fingers bruised from being wedged in tiny crevices. After scaling the rocks they pause a moment, taking large swigs from Strange's water-bottle. It is almost unbearably hot up here, at the foot of a shaded forest slope. They sweat almost feverishly.

'The roc must live up here somewhere. It'd certainly be left undisturbed,' Bowvayne gasps, the thrill of the chase still buoying up his exhausted body.

Jayasundera couldn't agree more. 'Yeah, we're the only ones dumb enough to come all the way up here and annoy it.'

'It might just have flown straight across the top of the island without stopping, you know,' snaps Strange sardonically. 'It may be in Mauritius by now.'

'You don't really think that, do you?' Bowvayne asks, crestfallen.

'Probably not,' Strange answers wearily. He watches the sun dipping into the turquoise ocean, and the yacht bobbing there like a white swan. 'Let's keep going,' he says finally.

They struggle up the steep hillside, the towering takamaka trees and the casuarinas with their branches like horse-tails soon replaced by thick, moist and shadowy jungle. It is more humid still. Bowvayne sees a giant land tortoise arch an imaginary eyebrow at him, and lumber with great dignity into the luxuriant undergrowth.

A waterfall tumbles down the hill in front of them. They stop briefly to drink from it and splash each other. Then onward again. Despite the heat the three of them are still aware of the tropical paradise's splendour; the exotic and colourful flowers, the scent of vanilla from the climbing orchid that gives us the famous flavour, the mango and banana trees, the . . .

'Eureka!' shrieks Strange, almost hysterical with joy. He is a little way ahead of his companions.

Bowvayne and Jayasundera rush to join him. 'It's the roc, isn't it?' hisses Jayasundera, looking around.

'Where is it? Where is it?' demands Bowvayne, his face a sheen of sweat.

'No no. It's not the roc, it's this,' Strange explains, indicating what he's cradling lovingly in his arms. Nestled like a baby is a large pale fruit he's just plucked from a tree nearby. 'Now I'll be able to have my breadfruit curry!'

'You cretin!' Bowvayne retorts, disgusted. 'You had us all going there . . .'

Strange is about to justify himself when he catches a slight movement out of the corner of his eye. 'Shhh!' he demands.

'What is it?'

Again. 'Shhh!' Something is flapping about just ahead, where there is a small jungle clearing.

They take one – two steps closer. A glimpse of a powerfully beating underwing, black with white primary feathers at the wingtips.

There is a sound like a wet sponge being dropped on a linoleum floor. Then a harsh cry, 'Aek aek aek aek aek aek.'

Another step forward. They're perhaps twenty yards from it now. A momentary view of a murderously-hooked yellow bill and a head nearly the size of their own. There is a rather eccentric tuft of white feathers above each eye, giving the appearance of pale eyebrows on an all-black face.

This must be the roc they've been searching for. It is tearing skin from an animal of some sort. Strange reaches into his backpack for his camera. Somehow they know it's sensed them. Activity ceases. Everything goes quiet. The trio begin to circle round the clearing.

Suddenly, from out of the trees, a killing-machine of vicious talons and murderous beak blunders towards them. The bird must weigh fifty pounds at least!

Bowvayne, Strange and Jayasundera scatter out of its path with their customary expertise.

The roc spreads its stupendous wings and launches itself into awkward, ungainly flight.

The humans peer out from behind large banana leaves. They see the roc soaring majestically now — the wingspan around twenty feet — spiralling up through the currents above the island.

'I'll never forget this as long as I live,' Bowvayne says emotionally.

Jayasundera is as impressed as the Mythbuster. 'I can see why you guys do this sort of thing for a living now. That was unbelievable. Just unbelievable.'

Strange is trying in vain to photograph the now tiny dot as it disappears into the distance. 'Damn and blast!' he curses, disappointed. 'Another one that got away.'

'Who cares?' Bowvayne says irrepressibly. 'At least we know it exists.'

'I s'pose you're right,' says Strange, mellowing, 'And at least I didn't damage my breadfruit.' The other two groan.

In the jungle clearing they find the hammerhead shark, its stomach bloody and exposed, but otherwise intact. Bowvayne looks at the other two, grinning impishly. 'Anyone want a flake supper?'

As they make their way back down the steep hillside, Jayasundera asks, 'What now?'

Bowvayne has that mad gleam in his eye. 'Isn't the last island where the dodo supposedly exists meant to be around here somewhere?'

'That's a thousand miles south at least,' protests Strange.

'That's what I mean, "around here somewhere". What's a thousand miles between friends . . .'

MYTHBUSTER SUMMARY SHEET

THE ROC EXISTS

Expert in the strange and mysterious, Arthur C. Clarke once wrote, 'Would you care to guess how many kinds of unknown animals – ie creatures that have never been described by science – there still remain on this planet? A hundred? A thousand? The answer may well be in the millions . . .'

At first it would seem unlikely that easily the largest flighted bird on Earth could escape detection until now. But consider this: The komodo dragon – the largest reptile on Earth – was only discovered this century, 1912 in fact.

And it isn't as if the roc has just appeared from nowhere. The first clues to its existence lie in mythology, the seed of many truths.

Around seven hundred years ago, when Marco Polo returned from the Orient to tell Europeans of the roc, he believed they were real. Admittedly, their size and powers were grossly exaggerated but this often happens when feats of animals are passed down from generation to generation and into folklore.

The specimen the Mythbusters saw that evening may be one of just, say, twenty that still lives. Sadly, it is an all-too-common trend that the specialised hunters at the top of the food chain – eg. lions, tigers, leopards, bears, sharks, the Tasmanian Tiger, eagles and other birds of prey – are dwindling in numbers for any number of reasons.

These twenty are living remote and isolated in one of the last places inaccessible to the marauding waves of Mankind – tiny, uninhabited islands surrounded by the vast ocean. Here they live in near anonymity, with just a few fishermen knowing of these majestic birds.

One last point, and an optimistic one, too. The bird the Mythbusters saw was partially covered with greyish fluffy down. Most ornithologists would allow us to make the assumption that this is a sign our roc was immature. This means these undiscovered birds are still actually breeding. But how big are its parents?

CLAPHAM WOOD REVISITED

MYTHBUSTER WORKSHEET

CASE: Clapham Wood Revisited

CODE: 003E 010891

LOCATION: Clapham Wood, Sussex, England.

MYTHBUSTERS: Bowvayne
Ian Digweed
Chris Strange

GUESTBUSTER: Les Hill, star of Aussie soap, 'Home & Away'.

TERRAIN: The wood is a densely-treed area. Surrounded by steep slopes and flat farm fields.

TEMPERATURE: 30°C–0°C

DIFFICULTIES: Investigating the thick woodland after dark.

SIGHTINGS: Several hundred. Varied. UFO sightings. Evidence of radioactivity. Humans experiencing odd physical effects. Animals disappearing. In investigation 002E 010888 the Mythbusters suggested that the wide variety of bizarre occurrences was due to 'The Clapparition'; a hitherto unknown spirit/entity. Subsequent information means a new investigation is imperative.

ACTION: Establish just what The Clapparition is. Prove there is a thread through the differing mysteries.

NOTE

As long ago as August 1988, just before the Mythbusters' first investigation of Clapham Wood, I met Charles Walker. He is one of the co-authors of "The Demonic Connection", a book which, among other things, details the mysterious occurrences in that weird wood.

He impressed me with his knowledge of the place and the sheer 'leg work' he had done. I invited him along to Clapham Wood when the Mythbusters were interviewed for the TVS "Coast to Coast" programme.

When interviewed, Walker painted a sinister picture where the many strange incidents over the decades were linked by a common thread — black magic and pagan worship. Perhaps not surprisingly, this lightweight regional news programme didn't put his alarming views to air.

Apart from one brief visit to the United Kingdom in January 1989, specifically to continue the Clapham Wood investigation, I wasn't in the country for well over two years. So unfortunately I missed the chance to purchase a copy of "The Demonic Connection".

When I was sent a copy in early 1991, I was amazed to find the authors' discoveries, experiences and conclusions were so close to our own, even though it was from quite separate research some years before us. The Mythbusters felt that this 'new' information prompted a new investigation.

While I don't agree with all the assumptions made in "The Demonic Connection", I recommend it to anyone interested in further Clapham Wood folklore. But this book is definitely not for the faint-hearted. And kids! Please ask your parents if you're allowed to read this one first.

Bowvayne
Bangkok 1992

I agree with everything Bowvayne has said above.

Chris Strange
Bognor Regis 1992

ONE

The rain beats relentlessly on Mattie Deal's back as he trudges miserably down the busy A27 dual carriageway. The darkness has fallen quickly on this soggy October night, and each fat raindrop is illuminated in the approaching cars' headlights. He pauses a moment, and, hunched against the cold, he lights a cigarette, using his leather jacket as a windbreak. Friends are waiting for him at a pub in the nearby village of Durrington. He can almost taste that first pint of beer there.

Deal is a pale, thin-faced young man with a mop of fair hair and skinny as a scarecrow's skeleton. In his early twenties, he wears the mandatory uniform to conform with his peers, ripped jeans and a Heavy Metal tee-shirt – and his similarity to Animal from "The Muppets" is quite extraordinary. And Deal even plays the drums professionally, just like his illustrious puppet twin.

He is about to cross the road and walk down Titnore Hill when he sees something moving just ahead. A hedgehog waddling beneath a gate to safety. Beyond the gate is an uphill pathway leading into woods, and he can see the orange glow of a fire somewhere up there.

Intrigued by the scene, he decides to investigate. He clambers over the metal gate and advances slowly, his shoes squelching through wet mud and gravel. Although he doesn't realise it, he is on the track leading to The Chestnuts, the entrance to Clapham Wood that is infamous for its bizarre and supernatural occurrences.

The foliage is almost unnaturally dense in here, gorse and brambles one side, tall, twisted trees on the other – and they seem to crowd in on Deal.

With every step the trees become more gnarled, damaged and deformed, due partly to the 1987 hurricane but perhaps also the Wood's own inimical influence. The ravaged sweet chestnut trees, jagged of leaf and trunk, are indicative of the place's menace.

He reaches the crossroads where a number of footpaths meet. The fire burns right at its centre. It is a large fire too, more than six feet in diameter.

Squatting on his haunches, he warms his hands near the flames. But the young man is puzzled. Who would come right out here in the pouring rain to build such an impressive fire?

Suddenly, movement. Appearing from the undergrowth not twenty yards away. Something dark and insidious with a stooped-over gait. Vaguely wolf-shaped but standing nearly five feet at the shoulder, its body is misty, shadowy, insubstantial; but the flickering light of the fire seems to give it more substance as it pads closer.

Deal trembles in terror. He wants to run but his legs refuse to move. The thing has loped to the opposite side of the fire. It sees him. Weird red eyes glitter insanely in the amorphous head. It pauses. Poised to leap at him.

At that moment Deal runs. He runs shrieking, not once looking back. He runs all the way back down the track, over the gate and across the road. Then he collapses, blubbering uncontrollably.

This is just one incident related to the Mythbusters following their first investigation of Clapham Wood.

TWO

The Mythmachine clatters along the A280, still held together in one piece by a coat of rust and a rather gluttonous slice of good fortune. (The Mythmachine that is, not the A280!)

Inside, Bowvayne, Ian Digweed, Chris Strange and Guestbuster for the day Les Hill are all chattering at the top of their voices, no-one listening to anyone else in particular. The Mythbusters liked Hill immediately. His knowledge of the unknown, his sense of adventure and his wisecracks ever loaded like bullets in a gun are all qualities that would make him a 'natural' as a Mythbuster.

The Mythmachine seems to be trying to shake itself to pieces as it trundles through pretty Angmering Village.

'And I thought being the Mythbusters' driver was going to be a glamour job,' Digweed grumbles, disgruntled.

Strange is in the front passenger seat. 'Are you still in first gear?' he asks, inspecting the gear-stick.

'No.'

'Are you sure?'

Digweed is adamant. 'I've been in fourth and flat to the boards for ages. If I put my foot down any further it'd get run over!'

In the back of the car, Hill looks at Bowvayne accusingly. 'I thought you said for this case we were getting a Porsche.'

Bowvayne is looking hurt. 'No no. I didn't say Porsche, I said poor . . .' The rest of his reply is drowned out by the agonised shriek of brakes as Digweed taps experimentally on the pedal.

Instinctively, Digweed puts his hands to his ears. The Mythmachine lumbers on to the wrong side of the road, into the path of an oncoming . . .

'Lorry!' shrieks Strange, flapping in a frenzied funk.

Digweed swerves to avoid the lorry just in time. The Mythmachine stalls and judders to a halt. Three Mythbuster hearts have stalled and juddered to a halt.

But Hill doesn't even have a hair out of place when he asks, 'Chris, how did you know that truck driver's name was Laurie?'

THREE

> Go and catch a falling star,
> Get with child a mandrake root,
> Tell me where all the past years are,
> Or who cleft the Devil's foot.
>
> JOHN DONNE (1573-1631)

'Right, here's the plan,' announces Bowvayne, when Clapham Wood finally comes into view. 'I reckon we'll get more achieved in this investigation if we split up into pairs. Les and I will check out The Chestnuts. Chris, you and Diggers investigate Long Furlong.' Ever since Digweed told Bowvayne and Strange what had happened to a friend of his called Mattie Deal, their enthusiasm for another Mythbusting expedition to Clapham Wood had been redoubled.

After leaving the pair at the gate to The Chestnuts, Digweed and Strange drive for another two miles and park on a grassy verge off the Long Furlong road. They cross the road, crawl under a barbed wire fence and trudge up the steep hill that leads into Clapham Wood.

At the top of the hill the Mythbusters slump to the ground, exhausted. They lounge about admiring the view before them, their backs to the brooding wood.

The sheer slopes of the South Downs stretch away in every direction, gold-hued in the early evening sun. There are fields of every earthy shade, with fences criss-crossing them, Mankind's puny partitioning of Nature. Farmhouses are dotted about this lush and quilted landscape, lights just beginning to wink from within. There is one field - almost a perfect square - a blaze of brilliant yellow flowers. It is one of those glorious sunny May days in the English countryside when it is surely the most beautiful place in the world.

'It is beautiful, isn't it?' says Digweed.

'Yeah,' Strange agrees, sighing blissfully. He watches rabbits scamper and tumble with each other playfully. Dozens of them, all along the ridge.

When he sees his partner playing a pocket-size computer game he frowns with disapproval.

Digweed is shamefaced. 'I meant my new Game Boy is beautiful.'

'Come on. Let's go,' Strange says firmly.

They pick their way among the trees, Strange setting a brisk pace. The woodland floor is thick with bracken and, further on, a carpet of nodding, bell-shaped blue wildflowers. Bluebells. Bluebells in every direction as far as the eye can see. The ground is descending gradually, and as they go forward the trees become denser.

The atmosphere more stifling.

Strange falls to his knees. 'I don't believe it!' he exclaims so suddenly that Digweed is startled.

'What is it? What is it?' He crouches beside the older man, expectant.

'Just look at this.' Strange's voice is husky, awed. He is gently caressing a wildflower between his fingers.

'Is that all?' Digweed says disappointed. 'I thought you'd found a clue to the mystery or something.'

Strange is smug, every wrinkle smirking. 'It is a clue. Lucky for us that I know it is. Photograph it immediately, Diggers.'

Digweed blinks. This is a clue? Photographing weeds seems pretty irrelevant to him. With a face longer than a fiddler's bow, he takes the photographs.

Strange crows, 'I suppose you're wondering what this is,' only vaguely aware that Digweed has become surly.

'It's a witch's broomstick in disguise?' Digweed scoffs.

Strange caresses the plant gingerly again. 'Close!' Tufts of large leaves rise directly from the roots and bear purple, bell-shaped flowers on short stalks. He stands up and paces about, a frenzied whirl of emotions. 'This is a mandrake, almost unknown in the wild in Britain. So what's it doing here. . . ?' His words trail off as he becomes more thoughtful.

Digweed's mood has taken a sharp upturn, his eyes lighting up greedily. 'Hey, we could make a fortune if we sell it to a nursery! Right, let me dig weed then. Ha ha ha!'

He takes a small gardener's trowel from his rucksack. 'I still don't understand what it has to do with the case though.' Digweed has actually bent over the plant and is gently loosening the soil around it when there is a horrible scream and Strange hurls him to the floor.

'What the hell. . . ?' begins Digweed angrily.

They disentangle themselves, Strange trying to regain his composure. 'Don't you know the legend of the mandrake?' he asks incredulously. 'Apparently it shrieks when uprooted, and any who hear it are doomed!'

'Oh,' mumbles Digweed, thoroughly cowed. 'I'd best put this trowel away then.'

'Yes, I think you'd better.'

The pair walk deeper into the wood. Strange has recovered his poise and is now lecturing Digweed. 'The mandrake's man-shaped forked roots can grow to a yard in length and the plant has been renowned for its magical properties since ancient times. It is perhaps the most potent ingredient used by witches and warlocks for charms and potions, and can induce frenzy, delirium, insanity and death.'

'Nice.'

At that moment they hear agonised shrieking, like a tortured soul of the damned. Or a mandrake root being pulled from the ground. . . ?

The pair look at one another in horror. And sprint still further into Clapham Wood.

FOUR

After getting out of the Mythmachine just off the A27, Bowvayne and Hill climb the gate and walk up the path leading to The Chestnuts.

This is the scene of countless mysteries over the centuries. Where there have been sudden disappearances, strange symptoms and illness among dogs walked there. Where a mysterious mist suddenly appears and manifests itself into a predatory animal. Spectral bears, wolves and foxes have all been reported, Mattie Deal's the most vivid sighting. Where, in 1978, a member of the magic cult practising in Clapham Wood warned investigator Charles Walker not to interfere with them. He was told, 'We will stop at nothing to ensure the safety of our cult!' Walker says the cult is called the Friends of Hecate. Where the Mythbusters saw the manifestation they dubbed The Clapparition several years before.

Bowvayne is positively chirpy. 'Lovely evening, isn't it?'

Hill is as heedless of danger as his partner. 'Yeah, great!' he agrees.

They reach the spot where several pathways

intersect, walk up a grassy mound and bear right, every so often scrambling over the mighty trunk of a fallen tree. Just as they enter dense woodland once again, they see something very special. A powerful, barrel-shaped mammal with a white head which has a black stripe over each ear and eye. Very handsome.

'Wow! Look at him!' exclaims Hill.

'A badger. Meles meles,' Bowvayne says, showing off his meagre knowledge of Latin. Then, as an afterthought, 'I thought they were only supposed to come out at night . . .'

'Maybe it's moonlighting during the day,' quips Hill.

Soon it scuttles into the tangled undergrowth. They follow it into the unknown.

The Mythbusters spend another hour hacking through the wood. But nothing to report.

Hill pauses at the threshold of another stretch of overgrown blackberry bushes, looks at his cuts and scratches. 'Let's head to the right and cut across the fields. We've a better chance of meeting the other two that way.'

'Agreed.'

They reach the edge of the wood. Help each other over the barbed wire fence. Cross a large, downward sloping field. Into the wood again.

The pair are in the midst of one of their intensely analytical moods. 'Somehow The Clapparition is the cause of all the different things happening in this place. I'm just no longer sure how . . .' says Bowvayne thoughtful.

Hill offers another point of view. 'Maybe your Clapparition is itself only an effect – not the cause.

Perhaps the magic cult is responsible for everything, even that manifestation. Have you considered that, eh?'

Bowvayne greets this new theory with rapturous acceptance. 'Yes! Yes! Yes! Yes! Yes!'

'So you think I might be right then,' Hill grins, eyes twinkling.

'It would explain so many things. All the various mysteries, The Clapparition, the sinister stuff in "The Demonic Connection".'

'Shhh! Listen!' Hill orders.

Far off, they hear agonised shrieking.

The Mythbusters look at one another questioningly. What should they do? The screams are repeated every few seconds for several minutes – and freeze them to the marrow. And now the night is drawing its sombre veil over whatever lurks in there.

'Let's investigate, slowly,' Bowvayne says, caution tempering blind panic.

'O-Okay.'

As Bowvayne and Hill stumble through the twilight wood, they hear something. The sound of boots snapping twigs underfoot. Not their own boots.

They glance at each other again, fear in their eyes. 'Make a break for the clearing,' whispers Hill.

'I'll catch up with you,' says Bowvayne. He doubles back.

A man with a shotgun steps out in front of him. The man has a dark hood over his head. 'Hey, where do you think you're going?' he hisses.

Bowvayne tries to play it cool. 'Er, I was taking a walk and got lost.'

The man's voice is sibilant with menace. 'Well,

you're coming with me now. There are sssome people who would be interesssted to check the truth of your sssstory . . .'

No way, thinks Bowvayne. He makes a break for it, bolting like a rabbit for the clearing.

A shot rings out. Bowvayne instinctively throws himself to the ground, then scrambles to his feet and hurdles an electrified fence. He catches up with Hill and the pair slide into a deep gully to safety.

FIVE

Digweed and Strange are running along the bottom of a soggy gully.

'I don't think I can take any more frights,' gasps Strange breathlessly. Digweed grins inanely.

The pair get another fright anyway, colliding into two maniacs who'd suddenly appeared at the lip of the gully and slithered on top of them. They all end up in a tangled, soaking heap. Digweed, Strange, Bowvayne and Hill.

After a mixture of greetings and curses, the four of them nervously gabble their exploits at each other.

Bowvayne takes a swig from Strange's water-bottle. 'I think you two are safe for a while yet. That mandrake you're talking about is well over a mile away and Les and I have been hearing screams too. It's either got a hell of a loud voice or . . .'

'. . . It's something else making the noise,' Hill finishes.

'I think a man with a shotgun is more of a danger to our health than an old legend.' Bowvayne grins. 'Still, I'd like to know what was screaming though.'

'Crows?' ventures Digweed.

'They "caw",' says Bowvayne.

'The brakes on the Mythmachine?' Strange jokes.

'No-one would be dumb enough to steal it,' Hill replies wryly.

Bowvayne is still ruminating. 'No, listen. I reckon that somehow the man with the gun and the screams are linked . . .'

'Yeah, right. The man could be an armed sentry for the diabolical cult and the screams something being sacrificed,' Hill says chillingly.

'While it's still light. . . ?' Bowvayne begins, not entirely convinced.

'Just a theory . . .'

Strange interrupts them petulantly. 'I think we should go back and discuss all this in the safety of our office, not here. God knows what might be lurking . . .'

'Oh, no,' wails Digweed. 'Oh, no. I don't believe it.'

'What?'

'What?'

'What is it?'

The other three are whirling about, wide-eyed with alarm. Has the man with the shotgun found them?

'I've lost my Game Boy,' Digweed mumbles.

'You've lost the plot, you mean,' Hill says angrily.

Bowvayne exhales like a beach-ball being deflated. 'You imbecile, Diggers! You had us all going there,' he says, relieved.

A mournful Digweed reaches into his rucksack for

his lunchbox, and indulges in a bovine chewing on a malodorous fish-paste sandwich.

Strange is cackling uncharitably at the new boy's latest performance. 'Ian, you really are a legend in your own lunchbox.' Then he hauls himself up the side of the ditch. 'Come on. The car's at Long Furlong.'

The Mythbusters cross a large, fallow field, crawl under another barbed wire fence, stumble down a steep embankment and reach a high metal fence with yet more barbed wire across the top.

Monkey-like, Bowvayne, Hill and Strange shin up the fence, skilfully avoiding the spikes by launching themselves over when they're nearing the top and dropping with a teeth-rattling thump on the uneven ground on the other side.

Digweed continues his disastrous day by impaling himself on top of the fence. There is laughter from the other three. 'My clumsiness will be the death of me,' he says lightly, covering his embarrassment.

'Come on then, get down, Diggers. It's getting pretty damned dark,' says Bowvayne, not sure why Digweed isn't moving.

'I can't.' Still he flounders.

Hill and Strange are laughing hysterically.

'You told us you were high-jump champion at school!' Hill manages to say between guffaws.

Strange freezes, his mood drastically changed. 'What's that?'

They peer into the gloom. Even Digweed cranes his neck to see.

Movement. A dark shape looms towards them from the other side of the fence. Twigs snap underfoot.

Sweat forms on Digweed's forehead. 'Get me down quick,' he pleads desperately.

It's the man with the shotgun again.

Bowvayne grabs one of Digweed's arms, Hill one of his legs. They wrench him off the fence and the luckless Mythbuster crashes to the ground face-first.

Suddenly, another man appears on the horizon, this time their side of the fence. Another sentry. The four companions beat a hasty retreat to the relative safety of the trees, continue the hasty retreat up a hill. Along a ridge. There's no sign of the sinister sentries now.

When Digweed pauses to look back he can see a huge fire burning in the centre of Clapham Wood and many people there . . .

(NOTE. Hope you had a great day, Les!)

SIX

Bowvayne and Strange are sprawled on bean-bags, surrounded by piles of old books. They're in the middle of a heated discussion.

'It's a possibility, I'll admit,' Strange says grudgingly. 'But I'm always a wee bit concerned when the answer to a mystery is as wacky as the weird goings-on that make it one in the first place!'

'But that's just the way it is.' Bowvayne strokes his jaw. 'It's something to do with malefic energy being used by the Friends of Hecate. It's there in abundance in Clapham Wood. By tapping it they're unleashing a force which produces the harmful cramps and seizures in humans and animals when they inadvertently stray too near its source. The energy is the reason for the evidence of radio-activity, too. And Les is right. Like him I'm convinced the UFOs, and all the other "Clapparitions" are being manifested by the cult . . .'

'Hmmm.' Non-committal.

Bowvayne is in full flow now. '. . . And this malefic energy has been there for centuries. Over two hundred years ago an old woman saw what would today be called a UFO float down into Clapham Wood and the place was "filled with fumes that stinketh of burning matter". Although it's no longer clear what happened to her, as a result of her sighting she was either immediately "smitten of the palsy" or burnt as a witch.' He grins impishly. 'Neither of these fates is recommended.'

Strange gives him a sour look. 'And how do you explain the dogs disappearing? Pagan sacrifice?'

'Yes! Charles Walker was actually told by a member of the Friends of Hecate that every month a dog or a chicken was sacrificed as part of its vile rites.' Bowvayne goes off into the office kitchen and returns with a bowl of Strange's delicious homemade chicken soup. 'What they're doing is absolutely fowl!'

Strange misses the joke, fortunately. 'The Wizard of Oz and his merry men in Clapham Wood!' he says scornfully. 'As an explanation it's too unbelievable . . .'

'Unbelievable, maybe. But it's still the truth,' Bowvayne points out. He sits down on the settee, soup on his lap.

'I don't want to be called a crank,' Strange says fussily.

Bowvayne waves his arms around expansively. 'It's a mighty big Universe out there, still full of the unknown and the unexplained. And most people don't give a damn about any of it — and even less about whether the Mythbusters are pathological liars or just mad! We're adventurers, visiting the places where the mysteries hide. We don't demand to be believed. If they don't want to, that's up to them. And don't forget, Chris, Diggers saw the cult round the fire that night.'

'They might have been boy scouts,' Strange says feebly.

Bowvayne scoffs. 'Armed boy scouts?'

'The ones with shotguns might have been game-keepers.'

'I'm sure they were sentries for the cult,' Bowvayne says ardently.

Strange is becoming mulish. 'Or gamekeepers.'

'Sentries.'

'Gamekeepers!'

'Sentries!'

'Gamekeepers . . .'

Digweed walks into the office. 'Did you say Game Boy?' The other two groan. 'It's absolutely freezing outside,' he continues, unbuttoning his greatcoat.

'The car's ready?' Bowvayne says expectantly.

'Yes.'

'And all the rucksacks and equipment?'

'Yes.'

'Right, let's go!' shouts Bowvayne. They dash down the narrow steps of Mythbase (UK)-3 to the Mythmachine.

It is a chilly November night, many months since their scare in Clapham Wood. Since then they have searched in vain for more clues. Now fresh reports of activity have been coming in and it is time to investigate again.

But what awaits them? Boy scouts? Or something far more malevolent?

SEVEN

The Mythmachine trundles into Clapham Village's single street. It climbs eastwards out of the valley, with a few houses on either side, a little shop and a post office.

The Mythbusters leave the car at the top of the street and walk up a side road to the wood. From the houses there is the furtive movement of curtains. Suspicious villagers glowering at them.

'This is like the start of that film, "An American Werewolf in London",' Digweed says, giggling nervously.

Bowvayne's breath swirls out in heavy clouds in the freezing night air. 'I know what you mean. This place really is weird.'

They turn on to a narrow dirt track. 'I thought I saw something moving up there,' Strange whispers, his voice cracking with trepidation.

'So did I,' hisses Bowvayne. 'Silence from now on.'

'Yeah, we'd all better keep quiet,' Digweed booms in agreement.

'Shhh.'

Into the wood they go. Swallowed by total darkness.

Almost inaudibly, Bowvayne says, 'No torches, guys.'

They creep through thick woodland and undergrowth. On and on. Until finally, there's something moving ahead of them. A harsh human voice shouting. The Mythbusters stop and mill about uncertainly, having a fretful discussion in mousey whispers.

'I think we should go back to the car and talk about it,' Digweed suggests chicken-heartedly. The others scoff.

'I suggest Bowvayne scouts ahead and finds out what's going on,' Strange says gallantly.

Bowvayne nods resignedly. 'Thanks, Chris.'

He slinks as stealthily as a fox through the last of the trees to investigate. Another narrow track. And beyond, a church, starkly silhouetted by moonlight.

Just off the track, two men in dark hoods are unloading tall black candles from the boot of a car. A shotgun leans against one of the rear tyres.

'Black magic candles,' Bowvayne mutters to himself. He hovers, wondering what to do next.

Suddenly, fifty yards behind him, Digweed blunders over a fallen tree trunk and crashes to the floor. In this tense, silent atmosphere, the noise is eardrum-piercing in its loudness.

The two dark-hooded men look up, startled, aiming torches at full beam into the trees. They see Bowvayne. He is blinded momentarily by their combined light.

'There he is!' shouts the man with the harsh voice.

'A spy! Get him!' yells his huge companion.

Without thinking, Bowvayne bolts. As do the other

Mythbusters. The dark-hooded men plunge through the undergrowth, close behind them.

Just ahead of him, Bowvayne sees Digweed stumble and fall. 'My clumsiness will be the death of me,' he says sadly.

The Mythbusters break out of the prison of trees and sprint down the village street for the car.

Bowvayne is gasping and wheezing. 'Everyone okay?'

'Fine,' says Strange.

An awful truth dawns on the two of them at the same time. No Digweed. They're going to have to go back into Clapham Wood to find him. Where the evil Friends of Hecate wait for them . . .

EIGHT

'We've got no choice. We have to go back. We're the only ones who can save him,' Strange says, hiding his fright with a Winston Churchill stiff upper lip speech.

'Agreed,' agrees Bowvayne.

There is the thunderous sound of a shotgun being fired in the silent wood. 'Whoa! What the hell. . .?' Bowvayne cries, clutching at Strange.

Strange grins feebly. 'Someone being sacrificed?' He makes an alternative suggestion to his first one. 'On the other hand, we could always wait here until Diggers comes back. We've got more of a chance of meeting up here than stumbling about in the darkness and the thick woods.'

'No, come on. Let's go,' Bowvayne replies with more bravado than sense.

The pair skulk back into Clapham Wood. Through the unnaturally dense foliage again. It is particularly hazardous without torches. Carefully feeling their way over fallen tree trunks. The sky is cloudless and there is a biting chill to the air. There's no sign of their pursuers . . .

Bowvayne keeps edging forward. 'I don't like it. It's almost too quiet.'

Strange couldn't agree more. 'I know what you mean. We might be walking straight into a trap.'

Bowvayne attempts optimism, rather unconvincingly. 'Remember it's only me they saw. Maybe they think there was only one spy . . .'

A twig snaps close by. The Mythbusters freeze, not even daring to breathe.

They hear someone breathing in ragged gasps, mingled with unintelligible mumblings. A torch is switched on, exposing them. The figure groans and advances upon Bowvayne and Strange.

'Diggers?' hisses Bowvayne questioningly.

'Oh, thank God!' Digweed groans in relief again. He is badly frightened.

'Diggers!' Bowvayne says joyfully.

Strange is more practical. 'Turn off that torch, Diggers!' he snaps. Digweed obeys.

'How did you escape?' Bowvayne asks in wonder, giving his brother-in-arms a hearty slap on the back.

'That fall saved me,' he replies, his voice shaking. 'I couldn't believe it. I lay there without moving and they ran right past me. They could see you two running and followed, I s'pose . . .'

'Where are they now?' Strange asks tersely.

'They passed me again on the way back to their car. They think we were just kids. I heard them say so.'

Bowvayne gives them an enigmatic smile. 'Hey, that's a bonus, right?'

'Yeah,' says Strange, understanding him. 'Because if they think it's just a couple of kids fooling around in the woods, they won't be on their guard as vigilantly as they might otherwise have been . . .'

Digweed interrupts, scandalised. 'You mean we're going back again, now? You're both mad!'

Bowvayne doffs an imaginary hat to Digweed and offers a courtly bow.

'At your service,' says Strange, joining in the fun. Then he adds more seriously, 'Now we've got this far we may as well see it through to the end.'

The Mythbusters press onward, a reluctant Digweed bringing up the rear. They come to the last of the trees. The car has been moved further up the track. Across the narrow strip they go. Through a lych-gate and into the tiny grounds of the Church of the Blessed Virgin Mary. Gravestones gleam like molars in the moonlight.

That is when Bowvayne sees three figures walking purposefully across the dark field beyond the church-yard, and climb a metal gate in its top corner. It is one-thirty in the morning. 'Now what are they up to at this time of night?'

The Mythbusters scramble over a low wall and move on tiptoes across the field. As they approach the high metal gate, they can hear subdued conversation. They slink behind a small mound close by, the leafy shoots and tangled weeds sprouting from

89

it offering just enough concealment for the three of them.

There they stay for the next hour and a half. Watching the bizarre preparations and listening to the muttered chantings on the other side of the gate. Too tense and enthralled to realise they're freezing cold.

A number of shapes, probably circles, are drawn in the dirt by the three Friends of Hecate. They stand in the most central of these circles, ringed by black candles. A small charcoal fire flickers nearby, and thick, oily tentacles of smoke writhe from it. The cloying aroma wafts around the Mythbusters. Its effects are making them drowsy.

'That's the smell of the mandrake root,' Strange whispers gravely.

The chanting becomes more insistent. They hear words like, '. . . demons fleeing . . . attacks and appearances of evil spirits . . . new bag for the vacuum cleaner . . . treachery and discord . . .' and other similar utterances.

After a further fifteen minutes of this, Digweed starts to say, 'What a load of mumbo-j . . .'

An eerie red glow appears in one of the outer circles. There is a startling drop in temperature.

'Shhh.'

'Look.'

The red glow quickly gathers itself together and solidifies. First The Clapparition, a vast, shapeless alien. Then it forms its head. And, finally, the wolf-shape of Mattie Deal's worst nightmare. The chanting reaches a crescendo.

'Shall I risk a photo?' ventures Bowvayne, desperate to use his brand new infra-red camera.

'No way. They'll hear it click,' Strange says decisively.

The invocation stops. Replaced by rhythmic murmurings. They seem to be having a conversation with the 'thing' they've conjured up.

Then, the manifestation dissipates, and becomes a misty red outline once more, and as it floats upwards on the breeze, it disappears.

The Mythbusters decide they've seen enough. They race across the field, through the churchyard and the wood, clamber into the Mythmachine and trundle into the night.

They finally know who is reponsible for the many mysteries in Clapham Wood - and precisely how it is done.

MYTHBUSTER SUMMARY SHEET

WHAT ARE LEYLINES?

At the very least leylines, or 'leys' as we should more correctly call them, conjure up thoughts of a network of invisible lines across the countryside linking historic and interesting places. For the more imaginative, the original purpose of leys involved magical rites and pagan festivals dating back to prehistory ... Stonehenge is at the centre of a vast number of geometrical patterns and leys that are too exact to be anything but predetermined. Although most leys tend to be in the five- to twenty-mile range with anything from three to ten sites incorporated, there are certain primary leys that run for hundreds of miles ... There seems little doubt that we have grossly underestimated the skills of our ancient ancestors. When it comes down to it we have no real knowledge of what life was like, say, 4000 or 5000 years ago. All we have is individual theories worked out from what little archaeological evidence has been unearthed ... Prehistoric societies may well have had a grasp of natural sciences that our modern culture has overlooked ... Because the knowledge and principles they based their lives on does not fit in with ours, we tend smugly to assume they possessed no knowledge at all. Quite obviously this cannot be true. The large number of accurate alignments and leys show that a considerable knowledge of geometry and astronomy at the very least, were put to good use. One point we tend to forget is that it is only in relatively recent times that we have become an urban society. Despite our attempts to pollute and alter the landscape the elementary

cycles of the planet still function as they always did
. . ., (If) there is a huge number of interconnected
leys (worldwide), their importance must have been
very great indeed. One thing we can say for sure is
that with the passing of time, that importance has
been forgotten . . . Perhaps the real reason why so
many important ancient sites are on leys has
something to do with natural earth energy. Here the
question can be split into two: Are the leys channels
to convey the energy as it is received by our planet?
Or are they a marking system to show where it
flows? My own opinion is that the second hypothesis
is more likely. There is no doubt that leys are
important and have been known to be so for at least
4000 years, and perhaps much longer. It seems a
shame we have forgotten why.

THE UNKNOWN MAGAZINE. Leylines: Pathways
of Power. Issue 1. July 1985.

Alfred Watkins (1855-1935), was the most notable
early pioneer in bringing the existence of leys to
modern Man. Like him, the Mythbusters are convinced of their power. This is what the authors of
"The Demonic Connection" have to say:

'The more Watkins and his associates researched
into the enigma of leys, the more they became convinced that they were not just traveller's tracks laid
out as a network but that something far greater lay
behind them, for it was as if some sort of current was
flowing along these ancient pathways – unseen,
mysterious, but wholly powerful. The behaviour of
birds, bees and other animals in relation to their
pattern of travel and migration along a certain line,
were all noted . . .'

But what happens when modern Man, in his ignorance, blocks or interferes with the smooth flow of this natural earth energy? Like at Clapham which is the connecting point for leys coming from Chanctonbury Ring to Cissbury Ring, also places of mystery and weird activity?:

'This blockage was subsequently called by ley-men a "black stream", and not only did it poison the atmosphere but could even cause physical sickness to those living in the immediate area . . . Some of these leys (around Clapham) are blocked by man-made obstructions and must therefore be classified as "black streams". This concentration of soured ley power is a veritable hot-bed of toxicity, making Clapham an ideal centre for any who wish, and have the knowledge, to tap the supply for malefic purposes. Is this what the Friends of Hecate are doing?'

The answer to the question posed is ALMOST CERTAINLY. Surely there are too many similarities between the Mythbusters' experiences and "The Demonic Connection" for the sightings to have been anyone else except the Friends of Hecate at work. We can only wait and see what the results of their black works are.

THE MYTHBUSTERS ARE SURE THERE WILL BE DOUBTERS. BUT REMEMBER, MYTHFANS, YOU CAN ALWAYS GO TO THESE PLACES YOURSELVES – IF YOU DARE.

BIBLIOGRAPHY
(and assorted doffs of the cap to)

Clarke, Arthur C., John Fairley and Simon Welfare. Arthur C. Clarke's Chronicles Of The Strange And Mysterious. London: William Collins Sons & Co Ltd, 1987.

Drive Publications Limited (ed). AA Book Of The British Countryside. London: Drive Publications Limited, 1973.

Editors of Time-Life Books (ed). Mysteries Of The Unknown – Mystic Places. Alexandria, Virginia: Time-Life Books, 1987.

Estate of Robert Thurston-Hopkins for use of 'The Spectre Monk' photograph.

Ellis, Kirsten. The Maldives. Hong Kong: The Guidebook Company Ltd, 1991.

Hamlyn for permission to use front cover photograph from its publication.

Howard, Hamish and Toyne Newton. 'Under The Greenwood Tree', Out Of This World. Orbis Publishing Ltd, 1983.

McFarlan, Donald (ed). The Guinness Book of Records 1992. Middlesex: Guiness Publishing Ltd, 1991.

Newton, Toyne with Charles Walker and Alan Brown. The Demonic Connection. Poole: Blandford Press, 1987.

O'Donnell, Elliott (ed). 'The Churchyard Bride', Ghosts. London: W. Foulsham & Company Limited, 1959.

Wieland, Lin (ed). 'Leylines – Pathways Of Power', Essex: The Unknown, no.1, 1985.

Mythbusters can be contacted at . . .
PO Box 109
Rustington
LITTLEHAMPTON
West Sussex
England
BN16 3BF